D1196716

Discrete Dynamic Programming

Discrete Dynamic Programming is one of a special series of brief books covering selected topics in the pure and applied sciences.

Leon Lapidus,
Princeton University
Consulting Editor

DISCRETE DYNAMIC PROGRAMMING

An Introduction to the Optimization of Staged Processes

RUTHERFORD ARIS

University of Minnesota

BLAISDELL PUBLISHING COMPANY

New York · Toronto · London

A DIVISION OF GINN AND COMPANY

Ad

H. E. PIGGOTT

omnium magistrorum meorum
facile principem.

First Edition, 1964

93C77 LIBRARY OF CONGRESS CATALOG CARD NUMBER: 64-15976

Preface

The object of this short book is to introduce the method of optimization known as dynamic programming, as it applies to a process with discrete stages. It is intended to be accessible to the undergraduate or interested layman and to present the underlying notions as straightforwardly as possible. For some reason the principle of optimality, elementary though it be, seems to many to be as elusive as Rabbit's "Aha" was to Pooh. ("Modo ei videbatur id, quod Lepus sentiret, optime exponere, modo minime vero."*) I hope the detail that has been given in leading up to it will prove painful in the older, rather than the more modern, sense of the word.

To set the stage I have attempted to survey briefly some of the commoner methods of optimization in the first chapter. A typical example of a process for which dynamic programming is most fitted is then given and used to motivate the more abstract definition of the terms. This example is blatantly drawn from chemical engineering but is so elementary as to require no real knowledge of either chemistry or engineering. The common sense solution of this problem guides the way to the formulation of the principle of optimality. This basic example is further used to illustrate the value of graphical methods and to introduce the Lagrange multiplier.

I have endeavored to give some variety of example in later chapters, although I have done scant justice to the fecundity of the principle of optimality. The leitmotiv of Chapter 6 is the reduction of dimensionality, the most serious obstacle to the application of dynamic programming. Some of the techniques, which are introduced in a series of examples as the need for them is felt, are recapitulated at the end of this chapter. I hope the economist will pardon my obvious naïvety and occasional levity in bringing

* From the book *Winnie ille Pu*, a Latin version of A. A. Milne's *Winnie the Pooh*, translated by Alexander Lenard. Reprinted by permission of E. P. Dutton and Co., Inc.

these problems together under the heading of economics. He will easily discern the intrinsic power of the method and see its application in the light of his understanding of economic theory. The next two chapters give some examples drawn from widely different subjects, and the bibliography at the end of Chapter 8 alludes to several more. The fifty-odd references and like number of problems scattered through the book by no means cover the range of dynamic programming. Great service would be done to the subject if someone would compile a critical, annotated bibliography of it.

The final chapters are intended to tie up a few loose ends and introduce some of the latest topics of research. There is little, even here, that cannot be understood by anyone with a knowledge of elementary algebra and differential calculus. It is one of the fascinations of dynamic programming that, while its basic notions require only a clear head, its application to any particular problem may call on the farthest reaches of one's knowledge and imagination. Chapter 10 was rewritten completely during the course of publication to include some of the latest results due to Wilde and Nemhauser. I am greatly indebted to them for allowing me to include this material and for a most stimulating correspondence which cleared up my initial misconceptions and led to a deeper penetration of a region that is still not charted completely.

Versatile though he is, dynamic programming is peculiarly the province of Richard Bellman. It grew from the multifariousness of his interests and its development has been continually revitalized by his ideas. It is a pleasure to acknowledge my indebtedness to him and his colleagues: it will be seen both in general and in particular throughout these pages.

As usual my sister-in-law, Mrs. A. Blair, has done a perfect job of the typing and my wife has patiently put up with my preoccupation.

University of Minnesota *Rutherford Aris*
April, 1963

Table of Contents

CHAPTER 1. **WHAT IS OPTIMIZATION?** 1

1.1. Mathematical modeling 1

1.2. Direct calculation 3

1.3. Method of steepest ascents 4

1.4. Gradient-free and random search methods 5

1.5. Differential calculus 6

1.6. Linear programming 8

1.7. Nonlinear programming 9

1.8. Dynamic programming 9

1.9. The calculus of variations 10

Bibliography 11

CHAPTER 2. **THE DISCRETE DETERMINISTIC DECISION PROCESS** 13

2.1. Chemical reaction in a stirred tank 13

2.2. Chemical reaction in a sequence of stirred tanks 15

2.3. Definition of terms for the general process 17

2.4. Various modifications of the problem for the stirred-tank sequence 20

CHAPTER 3. **THE PRINCIPLE OF OPTIMALITY** **23**

3.1. A common-sense solution of the stirred-reactor problem 23

3.2. The principle of optimality 26

3.3. The dynamic programming solution for the general discrete process 28

3.4. Presentation of results 30

3.5. The economy of dynamic programming 32

3.6. Other forms of the problem for the stirred-tank sequence 33

Bibliography 34

Problems 34

CHAPTER 4. **GRAPHICAL METHODS** **37**

4.1. The value of graphical methods 37

4.2. The problem 38

4.3. A geometrical interpretation 41

4.4. A graphical presentation of the results 42

4.5. A graphical construction of the solution 44

4.6. Parametric studies 47

Problems 52

CHAPTER 5. **RELATED PROBLEMS AND LAGRANGE MULTIPLIERS** **53**

5.1. Dual problems 53

5.2. The Lagrange multiplier 54

5.3. The economic interpretation of the Lagrange multiplier 55

5.4. The formal application of the Lagrange multiplier 56

5.5. Linear programming 58

Bibliography 59

Problems 59

CHAPTER 6. **SOME PROBLEMS IN ECONOMICS** 60

6.1. Bottleneck problems 60
6.2. Reduction in dimensionality 65
6.3. The menace of the expanding grid 70
6.4. The control of economic trends 72
6.5. Another trick in dimensionality reduction 77
6.6. The control of competitive processes 80
6.7. Review of the techniques of dimensionality reduction 85
Bibliography 87
Problems 88

CHAPTER 7. **SOME PROBLEMS OF COMMUNICATION AND INFORMATION THEORY** 90

7.1. The gambler and the faulty telephone cable 90
7.2. The erratic channel 92
7.3. Communications through networks 93
7.4. Next best policies 95
Bibliography 95
Problems 96

CHAPTER 8. **MISCELLANEOUS PROBLEMS** 97

8.1. Fitting a curve with line segments 97
8.2. Some questions in reliability theory 100
8.3. Growth and predation 102
8.4. Jacobi matrices 105
Bibliography 107
Problems 108

CHAPTER 9. **CONNECTIONS BETWEEN THE CONTINUOUS AND THE DISCRETE** **110**

9.1. The continuous as the limit of the discrete 110

9.2. The discrete as a sampling of the continuous 112

9.3. Programmed temperature control for a batch reactor 114

9.4. Linearization 116

Bibliography 117

Problems 118

CHAPTER 10. **SOME EXTENSIONS AND LIMITATIONS** **119**

10.1. Counter-examples for feedback 119

10.2. Some extensions 123

10.3. The feedback loop, I. (Reversal of direction) 128

10.4. The feedback loop, II. (Absorption of branches) 131

10.5. The platitudinous principle of optimality 133

10.6. Countercurrent systems 134

Bibliography 136

CHAPTER 11. **SOME ASSOCIATED MATHEMATICAL IDEAS** **137**

11.1. A discrete form of Pontryagin's principle of the maximum 137

11.2. Related problems and formulations 139

11.3. Computational considerations 140

11.4. The maximum transform 141

11.5. The convolution property 142

11.6. An application of the maximum transform 143

Bibliography 144

Problems 144

Discrete Dynamic Programming

CHAPTER 1

What is optimization?

Even though this book is an introduction to dynamic programming it will be useful to begin by talking more generally about optimization and relating dynamic programming to the other methods that are used in the craft of optimization. For optimization is a craft, a work that requires skillful and imaginative use of a variety of tools, its ends serving some quite practical purpose but its execution giving scope to the aesthetic, as well as banausic, faculties.

If tradition is to be believed, Dido was an early and enterprising optimizer. Having bargained for as much land as could be surrounded by the hide of a bull, she proceeded to cut the hide into a long thin strip and lay it out in a semicircle with the diameter on the seacoast. In this way she enclosed the greatest amount of land, founded the city of Carthage, and prospered until she met a situation which not even "the euristic vision of mathematical trance" could resolve. Whether the story be true or not, the problem of maximizing the area under a curve of given length is one of the classic problems of mathematics.

Optimization, broadly speaking, is getting the best you can out of a given situation—an ambition common to most. In this endeavor experience and intuition often play a large part. Experience and intuition, though usually obtained more painfully, may be developed by mathematical insight; a considerable body of methods and results has grown up which is applicable to the problem.

1.1. Mathematical modeling

If mathematical methods are to be applied to a given situation, that situation must first be expressed in mathematical terms. The business of doing this is a craft in itself and one to which we can only make passing reference.

Even the simpler situations in economics, engineering, industry, logistics, or strategy (to mention only a few areas where the best is always in demand) turn out to be intolerably complicated when subjected to a careful mathematical analysis. This analysis consists in first breaking down the situation into its simplest component parts and then finding a mathematical description both for these and for their interactions. Experienced judgment is then needed to simplify the equations to a point where they are amenable to mathematical analysis without destroying some essential feature in the process.

The important thing in this modeling process is that the assumptions should be made explicit. It may be necessary to neglect a certain feature to reach equations that are sufficiently simple to solve, but this neglect, however unfortunate, must be intentional and not an oversight. It frequently happens that to get a set of manageable equations the final model is idealized to a much greater degree than one would wish. However, provided the dominant features are present, the resulting analysis is not valueless for it is very often true that a qualitative understanding of the real problem can be obtained from the quantitative solution of the idealized one.

Perhaps womanly intuition or mystic reverence for the circle inspired Dido, but if she had attempted a mathematical model she would have certainly have made some idealizations. Thus the land would probably have to be regarded as a plane, the shore line as perfectly straight, and the strip of hide as a plane curve. Taking one end of the strip to be fixed at a given point of the shore, the disposition of the strip could be described by the shortest distance between any point of it and the shore. If this distance were y and the nearest point on the shoreline at a distance x from the fixed end, the curve would be described by a continuous function $y(x)$, with $y(0) = 0$. To express the area between the hide and the shoreline and the length of the strip itself the tools of calculus are needed; the area A would be

$$A = \int_0^X y(x)\, dx$$

and the length

$$L = \int_0^X \{1 + y'(x)^2\}^{1/2}\, dx$$

where x is the distance between the two ends of the strip. In mathematical terms the problem is to maximize A for given L.

At the other end of the historical scale are the contemporary problems of missile guidance. Here the designer may want to know how to control the vehicle so as to make rendezvous with a satellite with the minimum consumption of fuel, or how to dispose the fuel between three stages so as to maximize the final velocity. The mathematical modeling process will consist in representing the effect of fuel burning or guidance control on the motion of the rocket, and to do this considerable simplification will be required. The model will be a set of differential equations for the position, velocity, and attitude of the rocket and the objective will be represented in terms of position or velocity.

Naturally we shall not treat examples of this degree of complication for the principles can be most clearly seen if the example is elementary. We shall try, however, to develop the model rather carefully so that examples drawn from any one field are understandable to the general reader or student of another subject. The basic mathematical knowledge assumed is an elementary understanding of calculus and ordinary differential equations (such as is supplied in the first two years of undergraduate work).

Granted that the situation and the objective to be maximized can be expressed in mathematical terms, we need to know what methods are available to find the conditions that achieve this maximum and which method is the most suitable to use. We shall review some of the available methods and although we shall talk about them in terms of mathematical models, some of the methods are available for use in the physical situation itself. Thus if we speak of direct calculation with the model this might correspond to direct manipulation of the control variables in the physical situation. The advantage of the model lies in the fact that the exploration can be made when the direct manipulation of the real system is either intolerable or too expensive.

1.2. Direct calculation

The mathematical model consists of a set of equations (algebraic or differential) in which the state of the system is described by some of the variables and the controls or decisions by other variables. In the most general case the objective to be maximized is also a function of all these variables. If a choice of the controlled variables is made, the equations can be solved and the objective calculated. Another choice is then made and if this gives an improvement this second choice is to be preferred to the first. If there are many variables to be chosen an uninstructed search of this kind is haphazard at best, and even if only one variable is involved the best sequence of choices is still desirable. This latter problem has been fully solved for the situation where the objective has only one greatest value within the permitted region of variation of the single variable. There are also methods of guiding the successive calculations of which the following is the prototype.

1.3. Method of steepest ascents

Suppose that there are two controlled variables x and y and that the objective to be maximized by the best choice of x and y is as in Figure 1.1. The contour lines are lines of constant value of the objective function and if a particular choice of x and y lay at the point A, movement to another point A' on the same contour would produce no change in the objective function. The best direction in which to make a move is the direction AB at right angles to the contour. A small change of x and y in the direction AB should

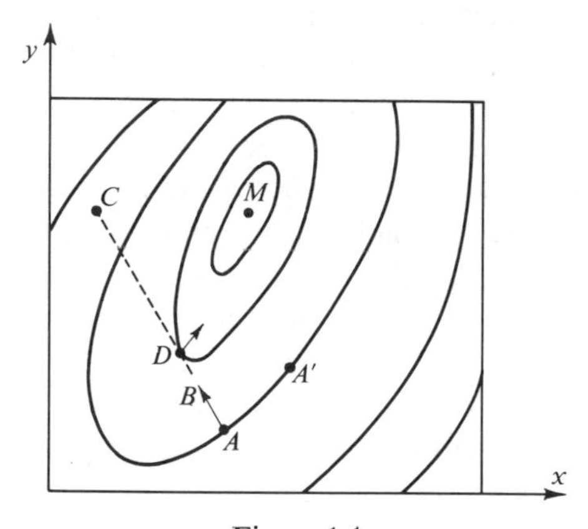

Figure 1.1

result in an increased value of the objective, though too large a change (namely, to the point C) may result in a decrease. If the surface can be expressed as a function $f(x, y)$ the tangent of the angle that AB makes with the x axis is $(\partial f/\partial y)/(\partial f/\partial x)$. Usually, however, this function $f(x, y)$ is not known, otherwise we could have recourse to differential calculus, so these derivatives have to be estimated. If A is the point (a, b) and δa, δb are small quantities we have the approximations

$$\left(\frac{\partial f}{\partial x}\right)_{a,b} = \frac{f(a + \delta a, b) - f(a, b)}{\delta a},$$

$$\left(\frac{\partial f}{\partial y}\right)_{a,b} = \frac{f(a, b + \delta b) - f(a, b)}{\delta b}.$$

Thus from calculation of f, the objective, at three points it is possible to estimate the direction of steepest ascent. A new set of calculations around some point in this direction (say, D) will give an estimate for the direction of steepest ascent. A series of trials of this kind thus lead to the neighborhood of the maximum M and to the choice of the x and y that achieves this. In the neighborhood of the maximum a more sophisticated plan of calculation can be used to get an idea of the shape of the maximum and to check that it is not a saddle point. This method was first extensively used in connection with the design of experiments where the objective function is not the subject of calculation but of direct measurement in a physical system. It can be readily generalized to a higher number of dimensions.

1.4. Gradient-free and random search methods

One defect of the method of steepest ascents is its sensitivity to scale factors. Thus it is clear from Figure 1.1 that the initial direction is rather

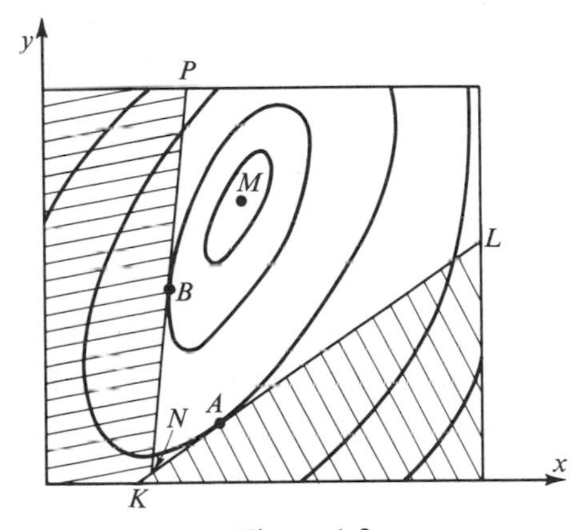

Figure 1.2

wide of the mark. If the y scale were compressed so that the contours were even longer and narrower a modest step might lead to a point like C which is actually inferior. Since the form of the surface is unknown there is no way of knowing whether the step we choose to make is large or small compared with the natural scale.

A method of overcoming this has been suggested by Wilde. Instead of looking for the direction of steepest ascent we look for the tangent of the contour and draw the tangent to this. The maximum (if there is only one) lies to the higher side of this and we can exclude the lower side from further attention. For a start at such a point as A of Figure 1.1 the line KAL in Figure 1.2 would be drawn and the area below it excluded. Another trial is now made at some point within the remaining area; a reasonable choice would be somewhere near the middle of it. Suppose B is the new point: a repetition of the process would exclude the area to the left of PBN. Clearly this process will gradually narrow down the region of search, and can be later profitably combined with a steepest ascent.

It is also clear that these methods may be misleading in case there is more than one maximum within the region of interest. For a steepest ascent started in the neighborhood of the inferior maximum would lead to the superior

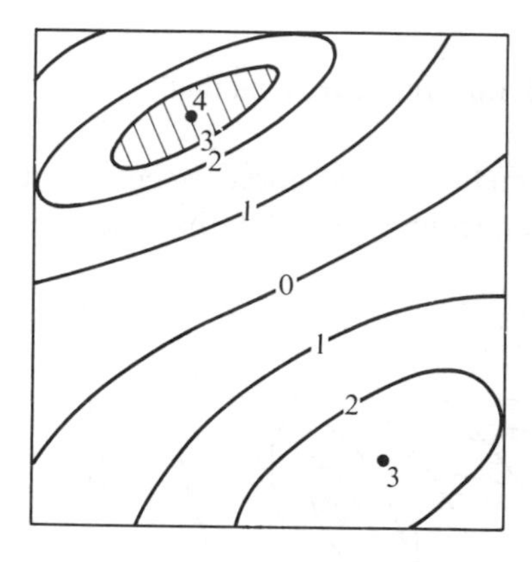

Figure 1.3

maximum being overlooked. The only way to guard against this situation (and fortunately it is not too common) is to introduce a random element into the search and every so often to try a completely random point. If this random point turns out to be more favorable than any of the others a systematic search can be started in its neighborhood. If the situation is as shown in Figure 1.3, there is evidently a probability equal to the ratio of the area about the highest peak which lies above the next highest (shown shaded) to the total area that a random point will find the highest peak. However, this is difficult to generalize to a larger number of dimensions.

1.5. Differential calculus

If we have given pride of place to the methods of direct calculation it is not with the intention of neglecting the classical techniques of the differential calculus. It is because the advent of modern computing machinery has made direct calculation of greater practical significance than ever before, particularly as it can handle functions of a complexity that prohibits analytical treatment. The methods of calculus are sufficiently well known that they can be mentioned briefly and we shall tend to emphasize the difficulties that beset them. These difficulties are associated with the fact that we often seek the greatest or least value of a function and not just a local maximum or minimum.

Consider the continuous function $y = f(x)$ defined on the interval (a, b) with a graph as in Figure 1.4. If we seek the points at which $f'(x)$, the derivative of y with respect to x, is zero we shall find values of x corresponding to the points B, C, D, and F. A test of the value of $f''(x)$, the second derivative,

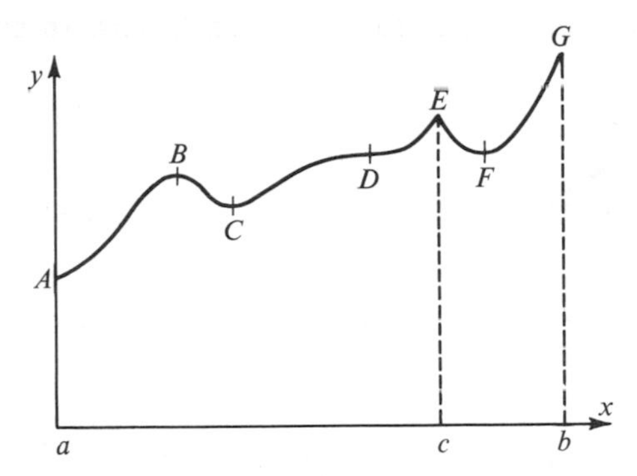

Figure 1.4

will show that B is a local maximum, C and F local minima, and D an inflexion point with an horizontal tangent. The formula for $f(x)$ should also reveal that although the function is defined on the interval (a, b) there are really two different formulas for the intervals (a, c) and (c, b), and $f(x)$ is not differentiable at $x = c$. For example, $y = |x - c|$ means $y = x - c$ for $x \geqslant c$ and $y = c - x$ for $x \leqslant c$. To find the greatest value of $f(x)$ in (a, b), we have also to consider the end points of the intervals within which $f(x)$ is differentiable. Thus the values of $f(x)$ at A, E, and G would all have to be compared with the value at the local maximum B to arrive at the conclusion that $f(b)$ is the greatest value.

This is a somewhat more formidable program than simply differentiating and setting the derivative equal to zero. However, there are cases where the physical nature of the function assures us that it is continuous and differentiable and has only a single maximum or minimum in the interval of interest. In such a case the simple prescription is adequate and often the best way of finding the maximum. In the case of more than one variable the task of finding a maximum is even more formidable. The first derivatives have to be made zero and the definiteness of the matrix of second derivatives established at each solution; then the boundaries of each region of differentiability must be searched and compared with the internal extrema. Again there are cases where physical intuition shows that a function must have a single internal extremum and here the vanishing of the first derivatives may prove the best way of finding it.

1.6. Linear programming

A situation where it is certain that calculus will be useless is the case of a linear objective function subject to linear constraints. In such a case it is

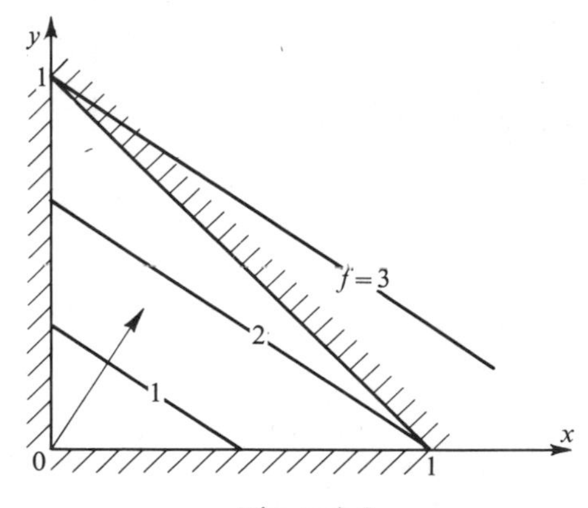

Figure 1.5

known that the maximum lies at a vertex of the permitted region. Consider the simple problem of maximizing

$$f(x, y) = 2x + 3y$$

when x and y must obey the constraints

$$x \geqslant 0, \qquad y \geqslant 0, \qquad x + y \leqslant 1.$$

These constraints define the triangular region shown in Figure 1.5 and the point x, y must lie in this region. Now the contours of constant $f(x, y)$ are the lines shown of slope $-\frac{2}{3}$. They are the level lines of a plane sloping upwards in the direction of the arrow and it is clear that the greatest value will be at the point where the triangle touches the highest contour; this is the vertex $x = 0$, $y = 1$. A little reflection shows that $x = 0$, $y = 1$ will give the maximum of $f = ax + by$ so long as $b > a$ and $b > 0$. If $a > b$ and $a > 0$ the vertex $x = 1$, $y = 0$ gives the greatest value, and if a and b are negative then the vertex $x = y = 0$ is best.

Naturally this example is the simplest of its kind. A more typical example is to find the maximum of

$$a_1x_1 + a_2x_2 + \cdots + a_nx_n$$

subject to inequality constraints such as

$$b_{11}x_1 + b_{12}x_2 + \cdots + b_{1n}x_n \leqslant c_1$$

$$b_{m1}x_1 + b_{m2}x_2 + \cdots + b_{mn}x_n \leqslant c_m.$$

Here the method of procedure is much less obvious, but a technique known as the simplex method has been developed that leads in a direct way to the solution. This is a standard tool of the economist, engineer, and operations analyst and is very widely used.

1.7. Nonlinear programming

Extensions of the methods of linear programming have been made to cases where the objective function is nonlinear and in some cases to nonlinear constraints, but this field is less completely surveyed than is the linear case. It is probably true to say that a quadratic objective with linear constraints is the only case treated with any degree of thoroughness. Linear programming can be presented as a case of dynamic programming but this is not usually a feasible way of doing the calculation. Nonlinear programming is equally readily adapted to a dynamic programming and this formulation is likely to prove more useful. What defeats the dynamic programming formulation is not the presence of a large number of variables $x_1, \cdots, x_n$, but rather a large value of m, the number of constraints.

1.8. Dynamic programming

Dynamic programming applies primarily to a situation in which many decisions have to be made to maximize the overall performance of a system, but the system is one in which distinct stages may be recognized and decisions at the later stages do not affect the performance of the earlier ones. It works best when the number of decisions at any stage is not too large and above all when the effect of these decisions can be represented in only a few variables. Under these conditions it can handle a very large number of stages with comparatively little more difficulty than a few. Since the whole of the rest of this book is concerned with this method we will not linger over the platitudes, except to point out that a continuous process can be regarded as the limit of an infinite number of infinitesimal stages. It is not surprising therefore to find that dynamic programming is an excellent way of approaching problems that are in the domain of the calculus of variations.

1.9. The calculus of variations

The problem that faced Dido was essentially one in the calculus of variations. An even simpler one is that by which the subject is usually introduced,

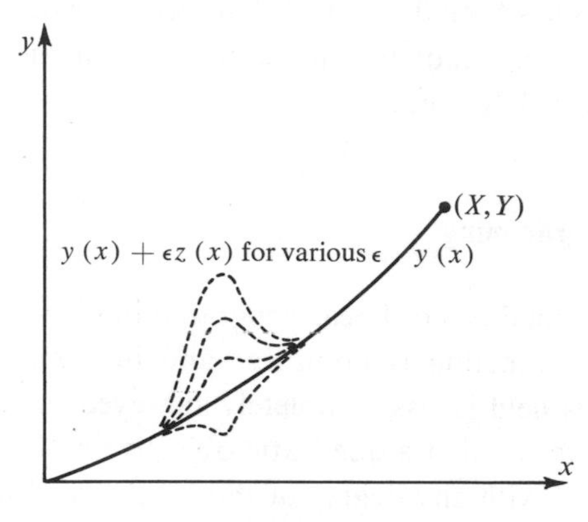

Figure 1.6

namely that of finding the function $y = y(x)$ between the fixed points (0, 0) and (X, Y), $Y = y(X)$, such that the integral

$$J = \int_0^X F[x, y(x), y'(x)]\, dx$$

is maximized. The usual method is to suppose that the $y(x)$ which does this maximization has been found. It then follows that any deviation from this $y(x)$ will give a smaller value of J. Now we can construct a whole family of deformations (as shown in Figure 1.6) by taking any function $z(x)$ which vanishes at $x = 0$ and $x = X$ and replacing $y(x)$ by $y(x) + \epsilon z(x)$. If we substitute this in the integral we have a new integral which for any given $z(x)$ depends only on ϵ,

$$J(\epsilon) = \int_0^X F(x, y + \epsilon z, y' + \epsilon z')\, dx.$$

Since $J(\epsilon)$ is maximum for $\epsilon = 0$, its derivative with respect to ϵ must vanish there. But

$$\frac{dJ}{d\epsilon} = \int_0^X \left[\frac{\partial F}{\partial y} z + \frac{\partial F}{\partial y'} z'\right] dx$$

and the second term can be integrated by parts to give

$$\int_0^X \left[\frac{\partial F}{\partial y} - \frac{d}{dx}\left(\frac{\partial F}{\partial y'}\right)\right] z(x)\, dx = 0,$$

since $z(0) = z(X) = 0$. Now if this is to be true for any $z(x)$ the expression within the square bracket must vanish everywhere, for otherwise we could contrive a function $z(x)$ that would make it positive. This condition,

$$\frac{d}{dx}\left(\frac{\partial F}{\partial y'}\right) - \frac{\partial F}{\partial y} = y''\left(\frac{\partial^2 F}{\partial y'^2}\right) + y'\left(\frac{\partial^2 F}{\partial y'\, \partial y}\right) + \frac{\partial^2 F}{\partial y'\, \partial x} - \frac{\partial F}{\partial y} = 0,$$

gives a second order differential equation for $y(x)$ which has to be satisfied subject to the boundary conditions $y(0) = 0$, $y(X) = Y$.

While this is straightforward enough it has, like the methods of calculus, some hidden difficulties. In the first place the solution of nonlinear differential equations with two-point boundary conditions is not entirely trivial. Then again there may be constraints which would force us to introduce solutions with sharp corners in them. These possibilities can be taken care of within the framework of the classical formulation, but at any rate from the point of view of trying to make the solution reasonable to anyone who is not a mathematician the approach via dynamic programming has distinct advantages.

Bibliography

1.3. The basic paper in the experimental application of steepest ascents is:

BOX, G. E. P. and WILSON, K. B., "On the Experimental Attainment of Optimum Conditions," *J. Roy. Statist. Soc.*, **B 13** (1951), 1.

There have been numerous descriptions and extensions of the method; see for example Wilde's book (Bibliography 1.4).

1.4. For this as well as an excellent description of other methods see:

WILDE, D. J., *Optimum-seeking Methods*. New York: Prentice-Hall, Inc., 1964.

See also:

WILDE, D. J., "Optimization by the Method of Contour Tangents," *Am. Inst. Chem. Eng. J.*, **9** (1963), 186.

1.6. The basic work is by G. B. DANTZIG, *Linear Programming and Extensions*. Princeton: Princeton University Press, 1962.

Elementary Introductions are:

VADJA, S., *Mathematical Programming*. Reading: Addison-Wesley Publishing Co., Inc., 1961.

———, *The Theory of Games and Linear Programming*. London: Methuen & Co., Ltd., 1956.

For an excellent discussion in the context of economics see:

DORFMAN, R., SAMUELSON, P. A., and SOLOW, R. M., *Linear Programming and Economic Analysis*. New York: McGraw-Hill Book Co., Inc., 1958.

CHARNES, A., COOPER, W. W., and HENDERSON, A., *An Introduction to Linear Programming*. New York: John Wiley & Sons, Inc., 1953.

WILLIAMS, J. D., *The Compleat Strategyst*. New York: McGraw-Hill Book Co., Inc., 1957.

The last book gives some excellent and entertaining presentations.

1.7. For an introduction, see

VADJA, S., *Mathematical Programming* (Bibliography 1.6).

A good review is to be found in

DORN, W. S., "Non-linear Programming—A Survey," *Management Science*, **9** (1963), 2.

1.8. The basic work here is to be found in three books by R. BELLMAN:

Dynamic Programming. Princeton: Princeton University Press, 1957.

Adaptive Control Processes: A Guided Tour. Princeton: Princeton University Press, 1961.

with S. E. DREYFUS, *Applied Dynamic Programming*. Princeton: Princeton University Press, 1962.

These are probably most easily read in reverse chronological order.

1.9. There are numerous books on the calculus of variations. For many purposes one cannot do better than to read the classical texts such as:

BOLZA, O., *Lectures on the Calculus of Variations* (1904), New York: Dover Publications, Inc., 1961.

CHAPTER 2

The discrete deterministic decision process

We shall start with a rather detailed presentation of a single example of the basic stagewise process. This is taken from the theory of chemical reactors, but is of so elementary a character that it will be understandable without any prior knowledge of chemical engineering. It has the advantage that it can be developed into an even more comprehensive case and leads naturally to the continuous process. It will be used to illustrate the definition of the basic components of the discrete decision process. These will then be defined more formally and illustrated by further examples.

2.1. Chemical reaction in a stirred tank

A chemical reaction is intended to turn certain raw materials into more valuable products and is often conducted in a large stirred vessel. The raw materials flow in and the product stream is withdrawn, the composition and temperature of the contents being kept uniform by sufficient agitation. Suppose that there is only one raw material A and one product B and that a and b denote their respective concentrations. The rate at which the reaction $A = B$ is going on is

$$r = k_1 a - k_2 b. \tag{2.1}$$

The constants k_1 and k_2 depend on temperature, but for the moment we will assume that the temperature is held fixed. This rate of reaction is the rate at which the amount of A per unit volume is being used up or the rate at which the amount of B per unit volume is increasing. Starting with a high concentration of A the rate of reaction will be large, but as A is used up (a decreases) and B is formed (b increases) the reaction rate will decrease until an equilibrium is reached at which $k_1a = k_2b$. Presumably the temperature has been chosen so that the values of k_1 and k_2 will give a food yield of B. Since whenever A disappears it reappears as B the sum of the two concentrations must be a constant; let us take the sum of the two concentrations to be the unit of concentration and write

$$a = 1 - c, \qquad b = c. \tag{2.2}$$

In this case c is just another symbol for b, the concentration of B, but it will also be called the extent of the reaction since it measures how far the reaction

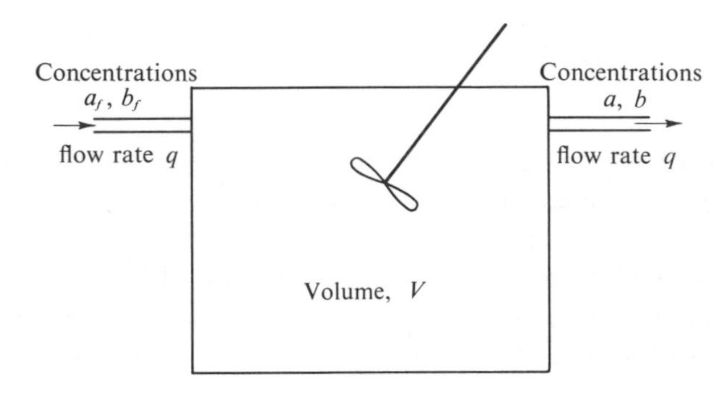

Figure 2.1

has progressed from A to B. The equilibrium extent, c_e, is the value of c when r falls to zero and this is

$$c_e = k_1/(k_1 + k_2). \tag{2.3}$$

We can write two expressions for the rate r, either

$$r = k_1(1 - c) - k_2c = k_1 - (k_1 + k_2)c, \tag{2.4}$$

or

$$r = (k_1 + k_2)(c_e - c). \tag{2.5}$$

If the tank (Figure 2.1) is kept at constant volume, V, the flow rate out of the tank must be the same as that into the tank. Let this flow rate be q and the concentrations of A and B in the feed be a_f and b_f and those in the product a and b. It is $(a_f + b_f)$ that has been taken as the unit of concentration and if the feed were pure A then $a_f = 1$, $b_f = 0$. Since the contents of the tank are well stirred the concentrations of A and B in the tank are the same as those in the product, namely, a and b. The rate at which B is being produced in this system is the difference between the rate at which it flows out and the rate at which it flows in, namely $q(b - b_f)$, and this must be the rate at which it is formed by the reaction. The rate of the reaction was said to be the rate at which the amount of B increased per unit volume, so that in a volume V the product B is being formed at a rate Vr. Thus we have the equation

$$q(b - b_f) = V(k_1 a - k_2 b). \tag{2.6}$$

This equation can be slightly simplified if we define the holding time of the tank to be

$$\theta = V/q, \tag{2.7}$$

which is evidently the time the system takes to "turn over" its contents. Then substituting from equations (2.2), (2.4), and (2.7) into (2.6),

$$c - c_f = \theta\{k_1 - (k_1 + k_2)c\}, \tag{2.8}$$

which is an equation for the product extent of reaction c in terms of the feed extent c_f and the holding time θ. It can be solved explicitly in the form

$$c = \frac{c_f + \theta k_1}{1 + \theta(k_1 + k_2)}. \tag{2.9}$$

We notice that only if the holding time is infinitely large does c achieve its equilibrium value, c_e; for finite θ, c falls short of this theoretical maximum. The reason is evidently that the reaction is being conducted at the same conditions as the product and since we saw that the reaction rate decreases as the product is formed this reaction rate will be very low and the holding time required large. But this suggests an optimization problem. Suppose the reaction were done in two vessels, the product of the first being the feed to the second, then, since the exit conditions from the first would be at a lower concentration of product, the reaction rate in the first would be greater than in the second. This would mean that either we should be able to get a greater concentration of B in the final product by splitting the available volume V into two parts, or we could get a given product with a smaller total volume by splitting the process into two stages. The question that immediately arises is, "How should the sizes be chosen to get the best out of the process?"

2.2. Chemical reaction in a sequence of stirred tanks

Let us consider a sequence of N stirred tanks and introduce a notation that will represent this compactly. The tanks will be numbered from the end to the beginning so that the first tank that the process stream enters is stage N and the final product leaves from stage 1 (Figure 2.2).

If the typical stage is stage n $(1 \leqslant n \leqslant N)$ its holding time may be denoted by θ_n and the extent of reaction in it (and hence in the stream leaving it), c_n. Since the feed stream to stage n comes from stage $(n + 1)$ the extent of reaction in the feed to stage n is c_{n+1} and it is quite consistent to denote the

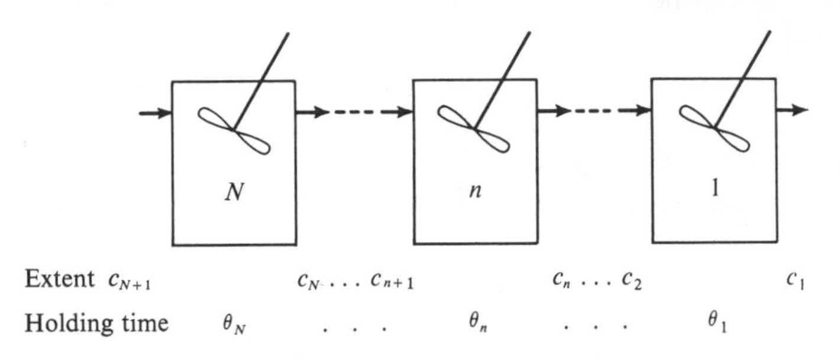

Figure 2.2

extent in the feed to the whole process by c_{N+1} even though the $(N + 1)$th stage does not exist. For each stage we can use equation (2.9) and hence

$$c_n = \frac{c_{n+1} + \theta_n k_1}{1 + \theta_n(k_1 + k_2)}, \qquad n = 1, \cdots, N. \tag{2.10}$$

Given the composition of the feed to the whole process, c_{N+1}, and the holding times of the reactors $\theta_N, \cdots, \theta_1$ we can use equation (2.10) to calculate successively $c_N, c_{N-1}, \cdots, c_1$ and so obtain the final product extent c_1.

Let us now fix on one optimization problem and use it to introduce informally the terms we wish to define. Suppose that the concentration of B in the final product must be γ if it is to meet specification; γ must be less than c_e. If the concentration of B in the feed to the whole process is β we may ask what choice of $\theta_1, \cdots, \theta_N$ will minimize the total holding time $(\theta_1 + \theta_2 + \cdots + \theta_n)$. Of course if there is only one stage there is no problem, for then $c_1 = \gamma$, $c_2 = \beta$, and equation (2.10) gives

$$\theta_1 = \frac{\gamma - \beta}{k_1 - (k_1 + k_2)\gamma}.$$

But if there are two stages a decision has to be made as to how to choose θ_2 so that the sum $(\theta_1 + \theta_2)$ is least. In general with N stages, $\theta_N, \theta_{N-1}, \cdots, \theta_2$ have all to be chosen and then θ_1 is fixed by the requirement that $c_1 = \gamma$.

In this problem the *state* of the process after the typical stage n is specified by the extent of the reaction or concentration of B, c_n; c_n is called the *state variable*. The *decision* to be made at each stage is the choice of holding time θ_n and θ_n is called the *decision variable*. When the state at the beginning of the stage is known and the decision for the operation of that stage has been made, the state of the process at the end of the stage can be calculated from a knowledge of the *transformation* that the stage effects. In this case the transformation is given by equation (2.10) in which c_n clearly depends on c_{n+1} and θ_n. The transformation will usually also contain certain *parameters* appropriate to that stage; in this case these are k_1 and k_2. The variables are also subject to certain *constraints*. On physical grounds we cannot allow negative volumes so that $\theta_n \geqslant 0$ is a constraint on the decisions. From the particular data of the problem we are required to make $c_1 = \gamma$ and this as we have seen means that θ_1 cannot be freely chosen. If there is to be an optimization problem there must be something to optimize. In this case we have the total holding time $(\theta_1 + \cdots + \theta_N)$, and this has to be minimized. The quantity to be maximized or minimized is called the *objective function*. In this case it is a function only of the decision variables, but in general it may also be a function of the state variables.

2.3. Definition of terms for the general process

The general process is shown schematically in Figure 2.3 and will be seen to generalize the simple example we have discussed. We will define and comment on the terms in more detail.

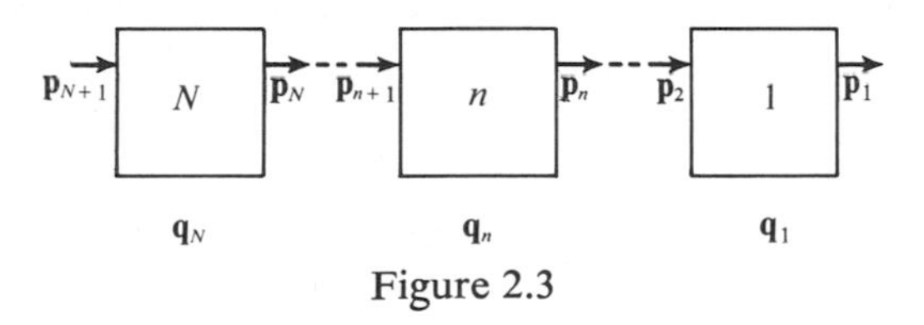

Figure 2.3

(i) *State*. The state of the material on which the process is operating is defined by a set of numbers called *state variables*. We use a suffix n to denote the values of the state variables after stage n. If s such variables are needed they may be written as a set $(p_{n1}, p_{n2}, \cdots, p_{ns})$, or more briefly by a bold face $\mathbf{p}_n$. This is sometimes referred to as the *state vector* or *vector of state variables*. In the previous example, $s = 1$ and $p_{n1} = c_n$. It is consistent with this notation that the state of the feed to the whole N-stage process is given by a vector $\mathbf{p}_{N+1}$, for $\mathbf{p}_{n+1}$ is the state of the feed to the typical stage n.

(ii) *Decision*. The *decision variables* are those quantities that can be controlled or chosen in the design and operation of any stage. If there are r such variables $(q_{n1}, \cdots, q_{nr})$ they may be regarded as forming a *decision vector* $\mathbf{q}_n$. In the previous example, $r = 1$ and $q_{n1} = \theta_n$. Sometimes a decision is more qualitative than quantitative in nature as, for example, the choice between two alternative procedures for transforming the state. If necessary such a decision can be quantified by calling one alternative $q_n = 0$ and the other $q_n = 1$; this can be generalized to a decision with more than two alternatives, and a computer program can very readily interpret such a codification. The set of all decision vectors $\mathbf{q}_1, \cdots, \mathbf{q}_N$ is called the *operating policy*, or, more briefly, just the *policy*.

(iii) *Transformation.* Each stage of the process transforms the state of its input into an output state in a way dependent on the decisions that have been made for the operation of the stage. We express this symbolically by writing

$$\mathbf{p}_n = \mathscr{T}_n(\mathbf{p}_{n+1}; \mathbf{q}_n), \tag{2.11}$$

meaning that given $\mathbf{p}_{n+1}$ and $\mathbf{q}_n$ it is possible to calculate $\mathbf{p}_n$. This may be a very simple matter as is the evaluation of a formula like equation (2.10) or it may represent a subroutine for a digital computer where many formulas are evaluated and put together. If the process is not as well understood as one might wish, $\mathscr{T}_n$ may represent the informed judgment of the man who has had the best experience in the operation of the stage.

(iv) *Constraints.* In general both state and decision variables may be satisfied by some constraints either in the form of equations or inequalities. We had these in the example in the form of $c_1 = \gamma$, $\theta_n \geqslant 0$. In the most general situation the constraints on the two sets of variables will be interdependent and this can be expressed by writing

$$\mathscr{S}_m(\mathbf{p}_1, \cdots, \mathbf{p}_N, \mathbf{q}_1, \cdots, \mathbf{q}_N) \geqslant 0, \qquad m = 1, \cdots, l. \tag{2.12}$$

In this general form the previous restrictions can be written with $l = N + 2$, as

$$\mathscr{S}_1 \equiv \mathbf{p}_1 - \gamma \geqslant 0, \qquad \mathscr{S}_2 \equiv \gamma - \mathbf{p}_1 \geqslant 0, \qquad \mathscr{S}_{n+2} \equiv \mathbf{q}_n \geqslant 0,$$
$$n = 1, \cdots, N.$$

However, in many practical situations the restrictions fall separately on the state and decision variables and often take the form of upper and lower bounds, as with

$$q_* \leqslant q_n \leqslant q^*. \tag{2.13}$$

A choice of decision variables that satisfies the constraints is called *admissible* and we speak similarly of an *admissible policy*.

(v) *Objective function.* If there is to be a optimization problem there must be some criterion by which various admissible policies can be judged. This has been variously called the profit function, figure of merit, and objective function. We shall use *objective function* for the criterion of the whole process, but we may also refer to it as being the sum of the profits from each stage. The word profit is to be understood in a very broad sense; it is not limited to any particular economic connotation. Thus in some cases we shall be concerned with maximizing a "gain" of some sort and in others with minimizing a "cost." In the previous example the total holding time was to be minimized. We shall see later how the objective function can be formulated for various related problems.

In the most general situation we might write the objective function as $\mathcal{O}(\mathbf{p}_1, \cdots, \mathbf{p}_{N+1}, \mathbf{q}_1, \cdots, \mathbf{q}_N)$, but in this expression the values of $\mathbf{p}_1, \cdots, \mathbf{p}_N$ can be calculated in terms of $\mathbf{p}_{N+1}$ and $\mathbf{q}_1, \cdots, \mathbf{q}_N$, by means of the transformations, so that we are entitled to write the general objective function as

$$\mathcal{O}(\mathbf{p}_{N+1}; \mathbf{q}_1, \cdots, \mathbf{q}_N). \tag{2.14}$$

A form that frequently occurs, and into which the general objective function can be put, is that in which the objective is the sum of profits from each stage. These profits can be expected to be functions of $\mathbf{p}_{n+1}$, $\mathbf{p}_n$, and $\mathbf{q}_n$, but again we can express $\mathbf{p}_n$ in terms of $\mathbf{p}_{n+1}$ and $\mathbf{q}_n$ and so we write

$$\mathcal{O} = \sum_1^N P_n(\mathbf{p}_{n+1}; \mathbf{q}_n). \tag{2.15}$$

If, for example, we wish to maximize $p_{11} - \lambda(q_{11} + \cdots q_{N1})$, where λ represents the cost of the decisions relative to the state, we may set

$$P_n = p_{n1} - p_{n+1,1} - \lambda q_{n1}.$$

It is true that the sum will then contain an additional term $-p_{N+1,1}$, but since this is the given state of the feed it is fixed and the maximum of ΣP_n will give the maximum of $\mathcal{O}$.

In general, we shall speak of maximizing the objective function, and this form of words will be held to cover the case where we are minimizing a "cost" type of objective function. To be strictly correct we could always give a negative sign to cost items and then maximizing them would be equivalent to minimizing their absolute value. The admissible policy $\{\mathbf{q}_n\}$ that maximizes the objective function $\mathcal{O}$ is called the *optimal policy*.

(vi) *Parameters.* The fixed constants of the system are its *parameters* and it is sometimes useful to list these. In the preceding example, k_1 and k_2 are the parameters, but when an example is generalized the original parameters may turn out to be functions of a new variable and new parameters. In general, it is good practice to reduce the number of parameters by forming dimensionless variables. Thus, in the above example, dimensionless holding times $(k_1 + k_2)\theta_n$

could be used and there would be only one parameter k_1/k_2 (or equivalently c_e). Even this could be removed by making $(c_n - c_e)$ a new variable, but it is well not to make a fetish of this as the physical meaning is liable to be obscured.

Setting up the problem involves a precise definition of these six component parts; the art of it lies in perceiving exactly what is needed in each case. We will illustrate this by first formulating two problems related to our previous ones.

2.4. Various modifications of the problem for the stirred-tank sequence

Let us summarize the basic example given in section 1.2 by listing the elements of the problem as defined in the preceding paragraph.

Problem Ia: Find the holding times, θ_n, $n = 1, \cdots, N$, of a sequence of stirred-tank reactors that will achieve a specified product $c_1 = \gamma$ with the minimum total holding time.

(i) State: c_n, the extent of reaction after stage n.
(ii) Decision: θ_n, the holding time of the stage ($N - 1$ values have to be chosen and θ_1 satisfies the condition $c_1 = \gamma$).
(iii) Transformation: $c_n = \{c_{n+1} + \theta_n k_1\}/\{1 + \theta_n(k_1 + k_2)\}$.
(iv) Constraints: $\theta_n \geqslant 0$, $c_1 = \gamma$.
(v) Objective function: Minimize $\Sigma_1^N \theta_n$ (or maximize $- \Sigma_1^N \theta_n$).
(vi) Parameters: k_1, k_2, γ (or equivalently $(k_1 + k_2)$, c_e, γ).

Another problem which we shall later show to be equivalent to this arises if we do not attempt to fix the final state as $c_1 = \gamma$ but instead maximize the difference between the "gain" of the reaction and the "cost" of the holding time. If we choose our units of value appropriately the "gain" of the reaction may be made equal to the change in the extent of reaction. Thus, since we denote the feed state to N stages by c_{N+1} and the product state is c_1, the net gain is $(c_1 - c_{N+1})$. In the same units let the cost of one unit of holding time be λ so that the total cost is $\lambda\Sigma_1^N \theta_n$. Thus the objective function is $c_1 - c_{N+1} - \lambda\Sigma_1^N \theta_n$ and this can be written in the form $\Sigma_1^N\{c_n - c_{n+1} - \lambda\theta_n\}$. Then we have:

Problem Ib.

(i) State: c_n.
(ii) Decision: θ_n (here all θ_n are chosen).
(iii) Transformation: $c_n = \{c_{n+1} + \theta_n k_1\}/\{1 + \theta_n(k_1 + k_2)\}$.
(iv) Constraints: $\theta_n \geqslant 0$.
(v) Objective function: Maximize $\Sigma_1^N\{c_n - c_{n+1} - \lambda\theta_n\}$.
(vi) Parameters: k_1, k_2, λ.

In this second problem the limiting case $\lambda = 0$ is not physically meaningful. For in this case the problem would be to maximize $(c_1 - c_{N+1})$ regardless of the total holding time. But c_1 can be made to approach c_e as closely as we please by taking θ_1 sufficiently large so that the answer to this problem is merely to let $\theta_1 \to \infty$ and then the objective function will tend to $c_e - c_{N+1}$. If $\lambda > 0$ this possibility does not arise, for if $\theta \to \infty$ the value of the objective function will certainly become negative. Another way to rule out the physically meaningless case is to maximize the conversion $(c_1 - c_{N+1})$ but insist that the total holding time should have a certain value, say Θ. In this case we should regard the remaining available holding time at any stage as a state variable, since it will govern the conversion that can be attained. Let $\varphi_n = \Theta - \Sigma_n^N \theta_m$, $\varphi_{N+1} = \Theta$. Then we have:
Problem Ic.

(i) State: c_n, φ_n.
(ii) Decision: θ_n.
(iii) Transformation: $c_n = \{c_{n+1} + k_1\theta_n\}/\{1 + \theta_n(k_1 + k_2)\}$

$$\varphi_n = \varphi_{n+1} - \theta_n.$$

(iv) Constraints: $\varphi_n \geqslant 0, \quad \theta_n \geqslant 0$.
(v) Objective function: Maximize $\Sigma_1^N(c_n - c_{n+1})$.
(vi) Parameters: k_1, k_2, Θ.

It has been mentioned that the parameters k_1 and k_2 are really functions of temperature. They take the form $k_i(T) = k_i^* \exp -E_i/RT$, $i = 1, 2$, where R is the gas constant. Let us suppose that the temperature T_n of stage n can be regulated; then it too can be a decision variable. If the cost of this regulation is neglected, we can draw immediate analogues of problems Ia, b, and c in which there are still more decisions to be made. Thus:
Problem IIa.

(i) State: c_n.
(ii) Decision: θ_n, T_n (θ_1 being fixed by the constraint $c_1 = \gamma$).
(iii) Transformation: $c_n = \{c_{n+1} + \theta_n k_1(T_n)\}/\{1 + \theta_n[k_1(T_n) + k_2(T_n)]\}$.
(iv) Constraints: $\theta_n \geqslant 0$, $T_* \leqslant T_n \leqslant T^*$, $c_1 = \gamma$.
(v) Objective function: Minimize $\Sigma_1^N \theta_n$.
(vi) Parameters: k_1^*, k_2^*, E_1, E_2, γ.

The analogous problems IIb and c can be generated by modifying the elements (ii), (iv), and (vi) in problems Ib and c.

A further modification might arise by trying to incorporate the fact that the regulation of the temperature involves a cost. If the reaction generates heat it will be regulated by a cooling jacket or immersed cooling coil that removes heat at a certain rate. The rate at which heat is generated is proportional to the rate of reaction, the constant of proportionality being the heat of reaction $(-\Delta H)$. Let C_p be the heat capacity of the reaction mixture so that when the stream flows into the reactor n at temperature T_{n+1} it brings in heat at a rate $qC_p(T_{n+1} - T_0)$ where T_0 is a reference temperature. The heat brought in plus the heat generated by reaction equals the heat going out with the exit stream, $qC_p(T_n - T_0)$, plus the heat that is removed by the cooling system, say Q_n^*. Thus,

$$Q_n^* = qC_p(T_{n+1} - T_n) + (-\Delta H)V_n\{k_1 - (k_1 + k_2)c_n\}.$$

If we write $J = -\Delta H/C_p$, $Q_n = Q_n^*/qC_p$,

$$Q_n = T_{n+1} - T_n + J\theta_n\{k_1(T_n) - [k_1(T_n) + k_2(T_n)]c_n\}. \qquad (2.16)$$

This equation can also be regarded as the transformation equation for temperature for given T_{n+1}, c_{n+1} and the decisions, θ_n and Q_n; it may be solved simultaneously with the mass balance equation to give T_n and c_n. Since the temperature of the feed will now affect the required heat removal it must be included as a state variable. If the "cost" of heat removal can be made proportional to its rate, a realistic objective function would be $c_1 - c_{N+1} - \lambda\Sigma\theta_n - \mu\Sigma Q_n$, since this is the gain by reaction minus the total cost of holding time and heat removal. We may thus formulate:
Problem III.

(i) State: c_n, T_n.
(ii) Decision: θ_n, Q_n.
(iii) Transformation: $c_{n+1} - c_n + \theta_n\{k_1 - (k_1 + k_2)c_n\} = 0$,
$T_{n+1} - T_n + J\theta_n\{k_1 - (k_1 + k_2)c_n\} - Q_n = 0$.
(iv) Constraints: $\theta_n \geqslant 0$, $Q_n \geqslant 0$, $T_* \leqslant T_n \leqslant T^*$.
(v) Objective function: Maximize $\Sigma_1^N\{c_n - c_{n+1} - \lambda\theta_n - \mu Q_n\}$
(vi) Parameters: k_1^*, k_2^*, E_1, E_2, λ, μ.

This has built the basic problem up into a fairly realistic form and we have here a sufficient variety of examples to show something of the craft of moulding the situation into its most suitable form. We will use these examples to show the fundamental technique of dynamic programming and return later to apply the principles we shall elicit to more diverse examples.

CHAPTER 3

The principle of optimality

We will approach Bellman's principle of optimality by way of a common-sense solution of our basic problem. Then, after discussing this principle, we will show in full detail how it is applied to the general problem and how the solution is obtained and presented.

3.1. A common-sense solution of the stirred-reactor problem

We are looking for the set of holding times $\theta_N, \cdots, \theta_1$, which will achieve the conversion $c_1 = \gamma$ from the initial extent $c_{N+1} = \beta$. We remarked previously that there is really no problem in the case $N = 1$, for the holding time θ_1 has to be chosen to meet the required condition:

$$\theta_1 = \frac{c_1 - c_2}{k_1 - (k_1 + k_2)c_1} = \frac{\gamma - \beta}{k_1 - (k_1 + k_2)\gamma}. \tag{3.1}$$

We thus know all about the minimum holding time for a single stage, and (γ being a parameter of the system and so a constant) we see that it can only be a function of c_2 or β. Let us retain the nomenclature c_2 and, instead of restricting attention to a single value β, let us remember that here is the solution to all problems with $0 \leqslant c_2 \leqslant \gamma$. In fact, let $f_1(c_2)$ denote the minimum holding time to reach $c_1 = \gamma$ in a single stage, then

$$f_1(c_2) = \frac{\gamma - c_2}{k_1 - (k_1 + k_2)\gamma}. \tag{3.2}$$

It need not trouble us that we have really had no freedom of choice here; θ_1 is what it has to be and is therefore the least that it can be.

If we go to $N = 2$ we see that there is a real problem of optimization. Whatever choice of θ_2 we may make will give some c_2 and the θ_1 that is needed to complete the process is given by equation (3.1) or (3.2). In fact,

$$\theta_2 + \theta_1 = \frac{c_2 - c_3}{k_1 - (k_1 + k_2)c_2} + \frac{\gamma - c_2}{k_1 - (k_1 + k_2)\gamma} \tag{3.3}$$

where c_3 is the given extent of reaction in the feed to the two stage process. But looking at equation (3.3) we see that the easiest way to minimize this is to regard c_2 as the decision variable which we are at liberty to choose anywhere in the range $c_3 \leqslant c_2 \leqslant \gamma$. Furthermore, it is evident that there is a value in this range, in fact in $c_3 < c_2 < \gamma$, which does minimize $(\theta_2 + \theta_1)$, for at the end points $c_2 = c_3$ or $c_2 = \gamma$ we have the same value, namely, $f_1(c_3)$ (for in these cases one of the stages has evaporated), and the expression is certainly continuous and differentiable. Thus to find the minimum we differentiate with respect to c_2 and set the derivative equal to zero.

$$\frac{d}{dc_2}(\theta_2 + \theta_1) = \frac{1}{k_1 - (k_1 + k_2)c_2} + \frac{(k_1 + k_2)(c_2 - c_3)}{\{k_1 - (k_1 + k_2)c_2\}^2} - \frac{1}{k_1 - (k_1 + k_2)\gamma} = 0.$$

Here is a quadratic equation for c_2 which can be solved as follows. Let $c_e - c = x$, $c_e - \gamma = \xi$, then since $c_e = k_1/(k_1 + k_2)$ this is

$$\frac{1}{x_2} + \frac{x_3 - x_2}{x_2^2} - \frac{1}{\xi} = 0$$

or

$$x_2^2 = x_3\xi. \tag{3.4}$$

Thus $(c_e - c_2)$ should be the geometric mean of $(c_e - c_3)$ and $(c_e - \gamma)$, and substituting back shows that

$$\theta_1 = \theta_2 = \frac{1}{(k_1 + k_2)}\left[\left(\frac{c_e - c_3}{c_e - \gamma}\right)^{1/2} - 1\right]. \tag{3.5}$$

If we similarly define $f_2(c_3)$ to be the minimum total holding time for two stages that will increase the extent of reaction from c_3 to γ, then

$$f_2(c_3) = \frac{2}{k_1 + k_2}\left[\left(\frac{c_e - c_3}{c_e - \gamma}\right)^{1/2} - 1\right]. \tag{3.6}$$

Having solved the two-stage problem completely, we may turn to the three-stage problem. If we write it out in full using the abbreviations $c_e = k_1/(k_1 + k_2)$,

$$(k_1 + k_2)(\theta_3 + \theta_2 + \theta_1) = \frac{c_3 - c_4}{c_e - c_3} + \frac{c_2 - c_3}{c_e - c_2} + \frac{\gamma - c_2}{c_e - \gamma}. \tag{3.7}$$

Here it is again best to take the intermediate extents c_2 and c_3 as decision variables; we could find the best values for them by differentiating partially with respect to these two variables, setting the derivatives equal to zero and solving the resulting equations. To do this without further thought may run us into some heavy algebra* so it is better to stand back and consider this more carefully. Suppose that some choice of c_3, $c_4 \leqslant c_3 \leqslant \gamma$, has been made; then the value of the first term in equation (3.7) is known and c_3 is fixed in the second term. But for any c_3 we know how to choose c_2 to minimize the sum of these last two terms and this is clearly the best we can do for this choice of c_3. Substituting the sum of the last two terms from equation (3.6), we have

$$(k_1 + k_2)(\theta_3 + \theta_2 + \theta_1) = \frac{c_3 - c_4}{c_e - c_3} + 2\left(\frac{c_e - c_3}{c_e - \gamma}\right)^{1/2} - 2$$

and now we may choose c_3 to minimize this expression, since it is the only variable left. We shall do well to work in the x variables and write

$$\frac{d}{dx_3}\left\{\frac{x_4}{x_3} - 1 + 2\left(\frac{x_3}{\xi}\right)^{1/2} - 2\right\} = 0,$$

that is,

$$x_3^3 = x_4^2\xi \tag{3.8}$$

and the minimum is

$$3\left\{\left(\frac{x_4}{\xi}\right)^{1/3} - 1\right\}.$$

Thus

$$f_3(c_4) = \frac{3}{k_1 + k_2}\left[\left(\frac{c_e - c_4}{c_e - \gamma}\right)^{1/3} - 1\right], \tag{3.9}$$

and

$$\theta_1 = \theta_2 = \theta_3.$$

By now a pattern has built up and it does not require much imagination to leap to the general case and write

$$f_N(c_{N+1}) = \frac{N}{k_1 + k_2}\left[\left(\frac{c_e - c_{N+1}}{c_e - \gamma}\right)^{1/N} - 1\right]. \tag{3.10}$$

This is the least total holding time required to reach the extent γ from the extent c_{N+1} in N states, and to achieve it the policy is to make the holding time of all stages equal.

* The example here is so simple that the algebra is not impossible, but a slightly more complicated example could easily produce algebra of insurmountable complexity.

To prove this, we proceed by induction and suppose that we know the best policy for $(N - 1)$ stages, whatever the extent of reaction, c_N, in the feed to these may be. We may write

$$(k_1 + k_2)(\theta_N + \theta_{N-1} + \cdots + \theta_1) = \left(\frac{c_N - c_{N+1}}{c_e - c_N}\right) + \left\{\frac{c_{N-1} - c_N}{c_e - c_{N-1}} + \cdots + \frac{\gamma - c_2}{c_e - \gamma}\right\}.$$

If any choice of c_N is made, the value of the first term is fixed, and by knowing the policy for $(N - 1)$ stages we know how to minimize the sum of the remaining terms. Using this optimal $(N - 1)$ stage policy means that the total holding time is

$$\frac{c_N - c_{N+1}}{c_e - c_N} + f_{N-1}(c_N)$$

and now it is only a question of finding the c_N which minimizes the sum of these two terms. The result of this minimization will be $f_N(c_{N+1})$, and so

$$f_N(c_{N+1}) = \underset{c_N}{\text{Min}} \left[\frac{c_N - c_{N+1}}{c_e - c_N} + f_{N-1}(c_N)\right]. \tag{3.11}$$

We leave it to the reader to confirm that the expression given in (3.10) does satisfy this equation and that the corresponding policy is to make all stages of equal size. For the moment we merely point out that by doing the problem inductively in this way we have only to choose one intermediate extent at a time instead of all $(N - 1)$ of them at once.

3.2. The principle of optimality

Often the most obvious fact is the most difficult to perceive and when isolated turns out to be more important than had been imagined. Bellman was the first to isolate the principle of optimality which gives access to the solution of a whole class of optimization problems and, though doubtless many others had used it in particular situations, he was the first to show how adaptable it was and how far reaching in effect. What we have done in the preceding problem is to replace the simultaneous choice of $(N - 1)$ decision variables by the successive choice of one variable. Since it is the simultaneous choice that involves so much difficulty the resulting economy is enormous and makes possible the solution of problems which would otherwise take a prohibitive length of time. The price that we paid for this simplification was that it was not until the last stage that we could set $c_{N+1} = \beta$, the particular value given in the original problem; until then we had to find $f_n(c_{n+1})$ for any c_{n+1} in the range (β, γ), since there was no way of knowing what c_{n+1} would be needed in the final optimization. There are situations where this price becomes exorbitant and we shall consider various ways of reducing it.

The classic statement of the principle of optimality is in the first of Bellman's books *Dynamic Programming* (Bibliography 1.8), page 83:

The principle of optimality: An optimal policy has the property that whatever the initial state and initial decision are, the remaining decisions must constitute an optimal policy with regard to the state resulting from the first decision.

Bellman calls this principle "intuitive," remarking that a proof by contradiction is immediate. The rather loose wording of this statement is said to be intentional and indicates that the user should think carefully before applying it. However this condition is not always met and it is perhaps worthwhile to bring out the implied conditions more explicitly and to give the proof, immediate though it be. We shall refer to decision processes such as we have been considering as decision processes without feedback, for in the general process of section 2.3 a decision $\mathbf{q}_n$ affects only the subsequent states $\mathbf{p}_n$, $\mathbf{p}_{n-1}, \cdots, \mathbf{p}_1$ and has no effect on the preceding ones. A coterminous subprocess of the N-stage process will be the n-stage process consisting of stages $1, 2, \cdots, n (n \leqslant N)$, and $\mathbf{p}_{n+1}$ will be called its feed state. The principle of optimality is that: In any decision process without feedback the optimal policy has the property that the policies for all coterminous subprocesses are optimal with respect to their feed states. The proof is by contradiction, for if this were not the case, say for the n-stage subprocess, it would be possible to increase the profit from the process by changing the decisions $\mathbf{q}_n, \cdots, \mathbf{q}_1$ to the optimal policy, and so the original policy would not have been optimal. This is true because the decision $\mathbf{q}_n$ does not affect the states or the profits from the stages $(n + 1), (n + 2), \cdots, N$. If there is feedback so that earlier states are affected by $\mathbf{q}_n$, then it is by no means obvious that a policy producing less than the maximum return from stages $n, (n - 1), \cdots, 1$ might not produce so favorable a return from stages $N, \cdots, (n + 1)$ as to make up more than the others lack. We shall reconsider the feedback case later.

We have perhaps belabored the principle of optimality a little heavily, but experience suggests that the student only grasps it thoroughly after a few iterations. It is really saying that if you don't do the best you can with what you happen to have got, you'll never do the best you might have done with what you should have had.

3.3. The dynamic programming solution for the general discrete process

The applications of the principle of optimality to the general process described in section 2.3 proceed in the same fashion as our common sense solution of the stirred-reactor problem. We start by considering only one stage in which the feed state $\mathbf{p}_2$ is to be transformed to $\mathbf{p}_1$ by the choice of decision variables $\mathbf{q}_1$ and maximizes the objective function $\mathcal{O}(\mathbf{p}_2; \mathbf{q}_1) = P_1(\mathbf{p}_2; \mathbf{q}_1)$. Let

$$f_1(\mathbf{p}_2) = \underset{\mathbf{q}_1}{\text{Max}}\,[P_1(\mathbf{p}_2; \mathbf{q}_1)] \tag{3.12}$$

be the maximum profit from one stage. It is obtained by the optimal choice of $\mathbf{q}_1$, which will depend on $\mathbf{p}_2$; let us denote it by $\mathbf{q}_1^0(\mathbf{p}_2)$. We are not here concerned with how this choice is made, but it must be an admissible choice, that is, satisfying any restrictions that are imposed. Now the objective function for two stages is

$$P_2(\mathbf{p}_3; \mathbf{q}_2) + P_1(\mathbf{p}_2; \mathbf{q}_1)$$

and if any admissible choice of $\mathbf{q}_2$ is made the first term can be evaluated. The $\mathbf{p}_2$ in the second term is given by the transformation

$$\mathbf{p}_2 = \mathcal{T}_2(\mathbf{p}_3; \mathbf{q}_2). \tag{3.13}$$

But we know how to maximize the second term from our study of the single stage process; $\mathbf{q}_1$ should be chosen equal to $\mathbf{q}_1^0(\mathbf{p}_2)$ and the resulting maximum is $f_1(\mathbf{p}_2)$. Now if we make various choices of $\mathbf{q}_2$ we should be able to arrive at the maximum of the sum of the two terms, that is, at the maximum of the objective function for a two-stage process. If we denote this maximum by $f_2(\mathbf{p}_3)$, this is symbolized by the equation

$$f_2(\mathbf{p}_3) = \underset{\mathbf{q}_2}{\text{Max}}\,[P_2(\mathbf{p}_3; \mathbf{q}_2) + f_1(\mathbf{p}_2)] \tag{3.14}$$

where $\mathbf{p}_2$ is given by equation (3.13). The optimal choice of $\mathbf{q}_2$, however found, will be a function of $\mathbf{p}_3$, say $\mathbf{q}_2^0(\mathbf{p}_3)$ and

$$f_2(\mathbf{p}_3) = P_2(\mathbf{p}_3; \mathbf{q}_2^0) + f_1(\mathcal{T}_2(\mathbf{p}_3; \mathbf{q}_2^0)). \tag{3.15}$$

We proceed to build up the optimal policy a stage at a time using the principle of optimality. Thus if the $(n - 1)$-stage policy for obtaining the maximum of the objective function $\Sigma_1^{n-1} P_r$ is known, this maximum value may be denoted by $f_{n-1}(\mathbf{p}_n)$. We can write the objective functions for n stages as

$$P_n(\mathbf{p}_{n+1}; \mathbf{q}_n) + \sum_1^{n-1} P_r(\mathbf{p}_{r+1}; \mathbf{q}_r),$$

and for any choice of $\mathbf{q}_n$ the first term can be evaluated; and so can $\mathbf{p}_n = \mathcal{T}_n(\mathbf{p}_{n+1}; \mathbf{q}_n)$. Thus the maximum of the sum of the remaining terms can be calculated, namely, $f_{n+1}(\mathbf{p}_n)$. It only remains to choose $\mathbf{q}_n$ to maximize the sum of the two terms and this will give $f_n(\mathbf{p}_{n+1})$. All this (which it is admittedly difficult to describe in words) is embodied in the equation

$$f_n(\mathbf{p}_{n+1}) = \underset{\mathbf{q}_n}{\text{Max}}\,[P_n(\mathbf{p}_{n+1};\mathbf{q}_n) + f_{n-1}(\mathbf{p}_n)] \tag{3.16}$$

where

$$\mathbf{p}_n = \mathscr{T}_n(\mathbf{p}_{n+1};\mathbf{q}_n), \qquad n = 1, 2, \cdots, N.$$

By definition, $f_0(\mathbf{p}_1) = 0$, so that equations (3.12) and (3.14) are included in this general equation as the cases $n = 1$ and $n = 2$. The decision vector that turns out to be the optimal one will depend on $\mathbf{p}_{n+1}$ and may be denoted by $\mathbf{q}_n(\mathbf{p}_{n+1})$. It is possible that $\mathbf{q}_n^0$ may not be unique but certainly $f_n(\mathbf{p}_{n+1})$ is unique, and the maximum being attained it matters not which alternative optimal policy is used, for, if it did matter, the objective function ought to take account of this.

Let us summarize the steps to be taken in setting up and solving the optimization problem by dynamic programming. The importance of steps C and D in the following list will be emphasized later; the presentation of results (step F) is the subject of the next section.

A. Check that the problem comes within the framework of the general process described in section 2.3. If there are any feedback loops a more careful analysis will be needed.

B. Set up the problem by listing the elements:

(i)	State,	(iv)	Constraints,
(ii)	Decision,	(v)	Objective function,
(iii)	Transformation,	(vi)	Parameters.

C. Check to see that the state variables are sufficient and that it is quite clear that the maximum of the objective function will be a function only of the variables $\mathbf{p}_{N+1}$. Define

$$f_N(\mathbf{p}_{N+1}) = \underset{\{\mathbf{q}_n\}}{\text{Max}} \left[\sum_1^N P_n(\mathbf{p}_{n+1};\mathbf{q}_n) \right].$$

D. Check to see that the decision variables are the most suitable so that the P_n are in the most readily calculable form.

E. Solve the functional equation

$$f_n(\mathbf{p}_{n+1}) = \underset{\mathbf{q}_n}{\text{Max}}\,[P_n(\mathbf{p}_{n+1};\mathbf{q}_n) + f_{n-1}(\mathbf{p}_n)],$$

$$\mathbf{p}_n = \mathscr{T}_n(\mathbf{p}_{n+1};\mathbf{q}_n)$$

for $n = 1, 2, \cdots, N$, starting with $f_0 = 0$.

F. Present the results in tabular or graphical form as described in section 3.4.

3.4. Presentation of results

To illustrate the presentation of the results let us calculate some numbers for the simple case presented in the first section of this chapter. If $k_1 = 0.8$, $k_2 = 0.2$, then $c_e = 0.8$ and we may take γ to be any number less than c_e, say 0.7. By equations (3.2), (3.4), (3.6), (3.8), and (3.9)

$$f_1(c_2) = 7\text{–}10c_2, \tag{3.17}$$

$$f_2(c_3) = 2[(8\text{–}10c_3)^{1/2} - 1], \qquad c_2^0(c_3) = (0.1)[8 - (8\text{–}10c_3)^{1/2}], \tag{3.18}$$

$$f_3(c_4) = 3[(8\text{–}10c_4)^{1/3} - 1], \qquad c_3^0(c_4) = (0.1)[8 - (8\text{–}10c_4)^{2/3}]. \tag{3.19}$$

The results calculated for the arguments $c = 0(0.1)0.6$ are given in Table 3.1.

Table 3.1

1	2	3	4	5	6
c	$f_3(c_4)$	$c_3^0(c_4)$	$f_2(c_3)$	$c_2^0(c_3)$	$f_1(c_2)$
0	**3.000**	**0.400**	3.657	0.517	7.000
0.1	2.739	0.434	3.292	0.535	6.000
0.2	2.454	0.470	2.899	0.555	5.000
0.3	2.130	0.508	2.472	0.576	4.000
0.4	1.761	0.548	**2.000**	**0.600**	3.000
0.5	1.326	0.592	1.464	0.627	2.000
0.6	0.780	0.641	0.828	0.659	**1.000**

In this Table, the c in the left-hand column is the argument c_4 for columns 2 and 3, c_3 for columns 4 and 5, and c_2 for column 6. There is no need for a column $c_1^0(c_2)$ since the conditions of the problem require this to be 0.7.

Suppose that we need the three-stage policy for $c_4 = 0$ (that is, feed of pure A). From column 2 we see that the minimum total holding time is 3.0; if we knew that the optimal policy was to have tanks of equal size this would mean that $\theta_1 = \theta_2 = \theta_3 = 1.0$. However, even if we do not know this we can find it from the tables. Column 3 shows that $c_3^0 = 0.4$ and this is the feed state to the subsequent two stages. Since these two stages must use the optimal policy with respect to their feed we have from column 4 with $c_3 = 0.4$ that $f_2(c_3) = 2.0$. Thus the minimum holding time for three stages is 3.0, while that of the last two stages is 2.0. It follows that the holding time of stage 3 is $\theta_3 = 1$.

Similarly in column 5 we see that $c_2^0 = 0.6$ and this is the feed to the last stage 1. The holding time for this is therefore $f_1(0.6) = 1.0$ and it follows that $\theta_2 = f_2 - f_1 = 1.0$. It would, of course, have been possible to tabulate θ_3, θ_2 and θ_1 and so have avoided the differencing, but in so simple an example this is unnecessary.

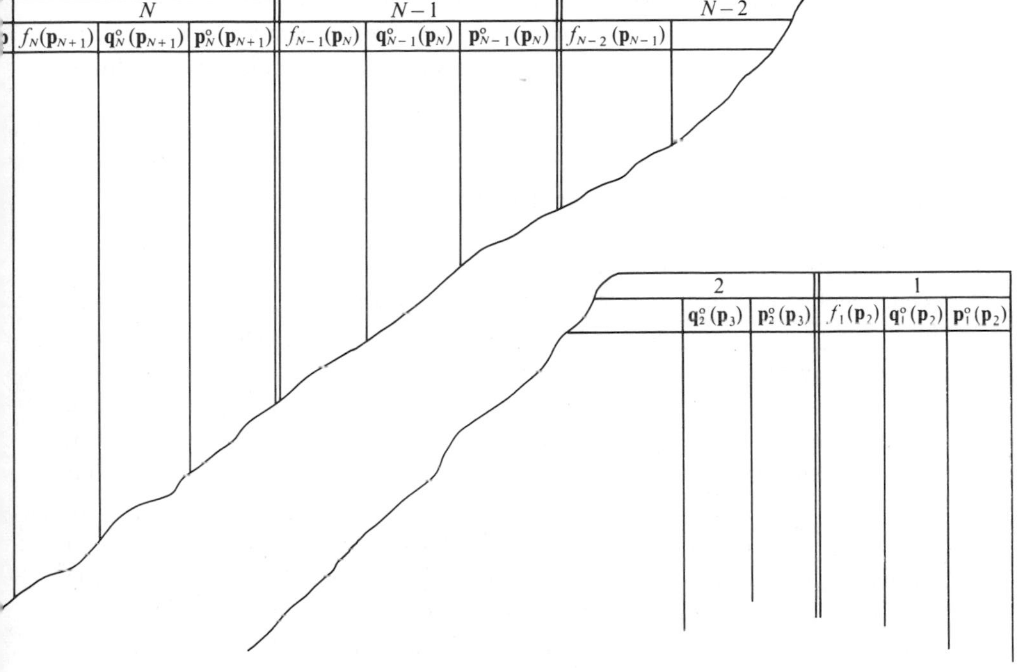

Figure 3.1

The solution to the general problem can be presented in a similar manner in a table of the form shown in Figure 3.1. At the entry for $\mathbf{p}_{N+1}$ we can read immediately the maximum of the objective function, $f_N(\mathbf{p}_{N+1})$ for N stages. In the next column the optimal decisions for stage N are listed and then the state resulting from those optimal decisions; $\mathbf{p}_N^0(\mathbf{p}_{N+1})$ has been used as an abbreviation for $\mathscr{T}_N[\mathbf{p}_{N+1}; \mathbf{q}_N^0(\mathbf{p}_{N+1})]$.

What is concealed in this presentation is the dimensionality s of the state vector $\mathbf{p}$ in the left-hand column. This is no trouble in the columns of this table for it is a small matter to have s columns side by side, but it is a real problem in the bulk of tables that it requires. If $s = 1$ everything is fine; a single column on the left at a sufficiently close interval for accurate interpolation is all that is needed. If $s = 2$ we have two variables p_1 and p_2 in the vector **p**, and this requires not a single column for varying p_1 but a set of them for each needed value of p_2. Thus instead of a single sheet of tables we would need many sheets, sufficient in fact to interpolate among them. But interpolation in two variables is messy compared with that in one. With $s = 3$ a large volume of tables would be needed and with $s = 4$ a library. Even if these tables are not printed out they have to be stored in a computer and here again, $s = 1$ is simple, $s = 2$ is cumbersome, $s = 3$ is perhaps just possible, and $s = 4$ is ridiculous. There is thus the greatest incentive to reduce the dimensionality of the state vector and we shall discuss some ways of doing this in a later chapter.

3.5. The economy of dynamic programming

Having recognized the difficulties that arise when the dimensionality of the state vector becomes large, let us now take a quick look at the reason why dynamic programming does offer such economy of calculation. This will also show the types of problem for which it is best suited.

In an N-stage process with r decisions to be made at each stage, there are a total of Nr choices. Suppose for the sake of uniformity that examining 10 values of each variable would allow us to decide with sufficient accuracy what the optimal value of each should be. If we were to proceed by an exhaustive calculation of all the combinations, 10^{Nr} evaluations of the objective function would be needed before the optimal combination would be found. If the optimal policy were needed for a whole range of initial states and again 10 values of each state variable sufficed, there would be 10^s initial states for which to determine the optimal policy. Thus the method of exhaustively analyzing all possibilities would require 10^{Nr+s} calculations. If each calculation could be done in 3×10^{-6} seconds on a machine with the very low rental of \$100/hr, the whole calculation would take $10^{Nr+s-13}$ years and cost 10^{Nr+s-7} dollars. Thus a five-stage process ($N = 5$) with three decisions per stage ($r = 3$) and one state variable ($s = 1$) would take a millenium and cost a space program!

In the dynamic programming formulation, 10^r calculations would be required at each stage for each state vector giving a total of 10^{r+s} calculations per stage. But this is the same for all stages so that an N-stage process would require only $N\,10^{r+s}$ calculations. At the same cost in time and money, $N\,10^{r+s-13}$ years and $N\,10^{r+s-7}$ dollars would be expended. For the previous case ($N = 5$, $r = 3$, $s = 1$) this comes to less than a tenth of a second and about half a cent!

Of course the comparison is unduly flattering for egregious folly is compared with moderate wisdom; but it would be unwise to suppose that folly of this magnitude is impossible.

However, if the numbers $N\,10^{r+s}$ and 10^{Nr+s} can be taken as representative of the two methods, the ratio $N\,10^{-(N-1)r}$ is some measure of the economy induced by the principle of optimality. Clearly the exponent quickly dominates the factor N and the economy increases enormously with the number of stages. What is not revealed is the difficulty involved in large s. Perhaps a more useful comparison would be the case with only one initial state, instead of the full range of 10^s states. In this case dynamic programming would require $(N - 1)10^{r+s}$ for the first $(N - 1)$ stages and a further 10^r for the last, a total of $\{(N - 1)10^s + 1\}10^r$. The exhaustive search would require 10^{Nr} and the ratio is $\{(N - 1)10^s + 1\}10^{-(N-1)r}$. Here the importance of s is indicated, but only partially. The real difficulty with large s is the storage space required and difficulty of interpolation. Bellman has called this "the curse of dimensionality."

3.6. Other forms of the problem for the stirred-tank sequence

The basic problem Ia (p. 20) was the one that we chose for illustrating the development of the principle of optimality. To emphasize the method of approach let us consider one of the other forms of the problem, say Ic. In this it will be recalled that we wish to maximize the yield $(c_1 - c_{N+1})$ having a fixed total holding time Θ available. Let us do the problem a little sloppily to begin with and see the importance of steps C and D.

There is no doubt that the structure of the problem is suitable for dynamic programming so that step A is no trouble. Suppose, however, we are somewhat hasty with step B and assume, as in the previous example, that the state is fully specified by the extent of reaction, c_n. We would then write the maximum of the objective function as

$$h_N(c_{N+1}) = \text{Max} \sum_1^N (c_n - c_{n+1}).$$

But on checking to see that the maximum will be a function only of the state variables (step C), it is evident that this is not so. For given only c_{N+1} the maximum yield is $(c_e - c_{N+1})$, where c_e is the equilibrium extent. But this requires an infinite total holding time, which violates the restriction on total holding time. Hence the single state variable c_{N+1} is not sufficient to specify the maximum yield, for this will depend also on Θ, the total holding time available. We are thus led to introduce the state variable φ_n which we had overlooked before. Thus

$$h_N(c_{N+1}, \varphi_{N+1}) \quad \text{or} \quad h_N(c_{N+1}, \Theta) = \text{Max}\,[c_1 - c_{N+1}] \tag{3.20}$$

is the correct way of setting up the maximum objective function.

In step D we check the decision variables to see that they lead to the most suitable form for calculation. With θ_n as decision variables we would have to solve the functional equation

$$h_N(c_{N+1}, \varphi_{N+1}) = \underset{\theta_N}{\text{Max}}\,[(c_N - c_{N+1}) + h_{N-1}(c_N, \varphi_N)]. \tag{3.21}$$

The calculation of φ_N is simple since $\varphi_N = \varphi_{N+1} - \theta_N$ but the calculation of c_N requires the formula

$$c_N = \{c_{N+1} + k_1\theta_N\}/\{1 + \theta_N(k_1 + k_2)\}. \tag{3.22}$$

If c_N is taken as decision variable, then θ_N has to be calculated from the formula

$$\theta_N = \{c_N - c_{N+1}\}/\{k_1 - (k_1 + k_2)c_N\}. \tag{3.23}$$

Evidently there is little to choose on the score of complexity of formulas in this case, for both c_N and θ_N will be bounded. In the more complex problem IIa to be considered in the next chapter, the variable c_n will have distinct advantage as a decision variable. The reason is that the equation of transformation is always linear in θ but may not be so in c. It thus is trivial to solve for θ given c but distinctly difficult to do the reverse.

Bibliography

3.2. The accessible locus classicus of the principle of optimality is in Chapter 3 of BELLMAN, *Dynamic Programming* (Bibliography 1.8), "The Structure of Dynamic Programming Processes." It was given earlier (1953) in a Rand Corporation report.

3.6. Various problems in the optimal design of chemical reactors have been given in
ARIS, R., *The Optimal Design of Chemical Reactors*. New York: Academic Press, 1961.

Problems

1. Solve problem Ic using the formulas of the previous section (3.6).
2. Show that this leads to the same policy as Ia.

3. The energy required to compress a gas from pressure p_1 to pressure p_{N+1} in N stages is proportional to

$$E = \left(\frac{p_2}{p_1}\right)^\alpha + \left(\frac{p_3}{p_2}\right)^\alpha + \cdots \left(\frac{p_{N+1}}{p_N}\right)^\alpha - N.$$

Show how to choose the intermediate pressures $p_2, \cdots, p_N$ so as to minimize the energy requirement.

4. A number of heat baths of the type that adorn the discussions of elementary thermostatics are connected by diathermal walls as below:

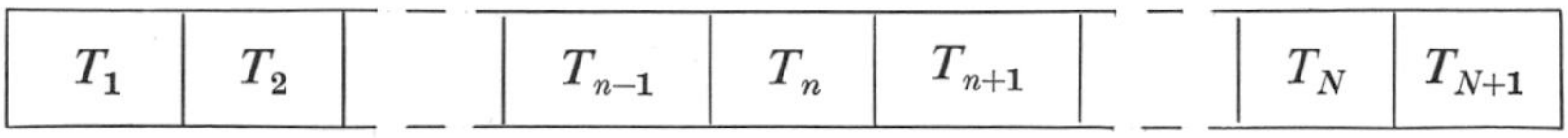

T_1	T_2	—	T_{n-1}	T_n	T_{n+1}	—	T_N	T_{N+1}

T_1 and T_{N+1}, $(>T_1)$, the temperatures of the end baths, are held fixed and the heat transmitted from bath n to bath $(n - 1)$ is $Q_n = k_n(T_n - T_{n+1})$. If the rate of entropy generation at each stage is the net heat flux over the temperature $(Q_{n+1} - Q_n)/T_n$, formulate the problem of finding the intermediate temperatures $T_2, \cdots, T_N$ that minimize the rate of generation of entropy.

5. If all the k_n in problem 4 are equal, solve the problem of minimizing the entropy generation.

6. A number of equal spheres are connected by light, inextensible strings of equal length. There are $(2N + 2)$ spheres and the end ones are placed on the same level at a distance apart of $(2M + 1)$ times the distance between the centers of consecutive spheres. Find how the spheres hang to minimize their potential energy.

7. A foundation has such insight into the proposals it receives and such foresight as to their results that it knows that x_n dollars granted to the nth proposal will yield a "benefit" $f_n(x_n)$. Set up the problem of administering the total budget X of this foundation so as to maximize the total benefit if it receives N proposals. What form of $f_n(x_n)$ is reasonable? How would policy decisions on the total amount of any grant affect the problem?

8. The "image" of the foundation is the sum of the "impressions" $g_n(x_n)$ that each grant makes. The functions $g_n(x_n)$ are monotonic increasing. Set up the problem of maximizing the benefit of its grants while holding its image constant.

9. In an N stage rocket the weight of the nth stage is a function of the velocity increase v_n that takes place during the firing of that stage and the weight w_n of the remaining $(n - 1)$ stages. Let this be $W(v_n, w_n)$. If $f_N(V)$ is the

minimum weight required to attain a final velocity of V with N stages, show that

$$f_N(V) = \min_{v_N} [W\{v_N, f_{N-1}(V - v_N)\} + f_{N-1}(V - v_N)].$$

Does this introduce any special computational difficulties we have not encountered before? [See Bellman, *Applied Dynamic Programming* (Bibliography 1.8), Chapter 6.]

10. A number of beads are in linear array along a composite elastic cord. The elastic properties of the cord vary from segment to segment. How are the beads disposed for minimum strain energy?

CHAPTER 4

Graphical methods

4.1. The value of graphical methods

Graphical methods have always held a great attraction for the mathematical practitioner. The pure mathematician may have cultivated the ability for abstract thought to a point where he needs no such crutch, but in attaining this maturity he has probably made considerable use of the geometrical presentation of abstract notions. Certainly from a didactic point of view the graphical method has very much to be said for it.

From the computational angle a graphical method must be looked at more carefully. The inaccuracy of graphical differentiation is notorious and the Jeffreys' call attention to a flaw in common graph papers that make them much less accurate than would be thought for integration.* With the advent of the high speed computer much of the chore of desk calculation has been removed and with it something of the advantage of speed and ease that the graphical method once held. In spite of this, however, there are still three good reasons for retaining a strong interest in graphical techniques. Firstly, their clarity of presentation often gives the best impression of the structure of the problem and its answer. Secondly, granting their very limited accuracy, they may still be useful for exploratory calculations that define a region to be later covered by more accurate calculation. Thirdly, an immense amount of information can often be compressed into a single graph and in a few graphs the economist or engineer may have the essence of a whole problem at his finger tips.

We shall try and show some of these advantages in this chapter by treating problem IIa in which both temperature and holding time have to be chosen for the optimum.

* H. S. and B. S. Jeffreys, *Methods of Mathematical Physics*. (2d ed.; New York: Cambridge University Press, 1950), p. 290.

4.2. The problem

Let us recall the problem briefly from its statement on page 21. In this problem the temperature is to be a decision variable and the reaction rate is a function of temperature through the $k_1(T)$ and $k_2(T)$. The equation of transformation can be written

$$c_n - c_{n+1} = \theta_n[k_1(T_n) - \{k_1(T_n) + k_2(T_n)\}c_n], \tag{4.1}$$

where

$$k_i(T) = k_i^* \exp - E_i/RT, \qquad i = 1, 2. \tag{4.2}$$

Let us denote the expression on the right of equation (4.1) by $\theta_n r(c_n, T_n)$. The objective is to minimize the total holding time subject to achieving the final conversion γ. As before, this means that not all the θ_n can be chosen independently, for one of them will be fixed by the requirement $c_1 = \gamma$; only $(N - 1)$ of the N θ's will therefore be choosable. Again, in view of the fact that θ_n is so readily calculated from equation (4.1) and the objective function involves only θ_n, it is convenient to treat the $(N - 1)$ intermediate extents $c_N, c_{N-1}, \cdots, c_2$ as the decision variables. These together with the N temperatures form the complete set of $(2N - 1)$ decision variables.

The problem may now be stated as follows: Choose the extents c_n, $n = 2, \cdots, N$ (subject to $c_{N+1} \leqslant c_N \leqslant \cdots \leqslant c_2 \leqslant c_1$) and the temperatures T_n, $n = 1, \cdots, N$ (subject to $T_* \leqslant T_n \leqslant T^*$) so that

$$\sum_1^N \left[\frac{c_n - c_{n+1}}{r(c_n, T_n)}\right] \tag{4.3}$$

has the least possible value. As before, we recognize that this minimum will depend only on the number of stages and the initial extent c_{N+1}. We therefore write

$$f_N(c_{N+1}) = \text{Min} \sum_1^N \left[\frac{c_n - c_{n+1}}{r(c_n, T_n)}\right], \tag{4.4}$$

where the minimum is obtained by an admissible choice of $c_N, \cdots, c_2$ and $T_N, \cdots, T_1$. For the particular case $N = 1$, since $c_1 = \gamma$ is fixed,

$$f_1(c_2) = \text{Min} \left[\frac{\gamma - c_2}{r(\gamma, T_1)}\right] \tag{4.5}$$

and only the choice of T_1 can be made. Applying the principle of optimality,

$$f_N(c_{N+1}) = \text{Min} \left[\frac{c_N - c_{N+1}}{r(c_N, T_N)} + f_{N-1}(c_N)\right] \tag{4.6}$$

for $N > 1$ and here the only choices to be made are of c_N and T_N.

Now it is to be noticed that in equation (4.6) T_N occurs only in the first term and then only in its denominator. Evidently if a choice of c_N had been made we could do no better than choose the T_N that maximizes the rate of reaction r. Now

$$r(c, T) = k_1(T)(1 - c) - k_2(T)c \tag{4.7}$$

where k_1 and k_2 are given by equation (4.2). For fixed c this has the form $\alpha A - \beta B$ where $A = 1 - c$, $B = c$, $\alpha = k_1$ and $\beta = k_2$. Problem 5, at the end of this chapter, considers the maximum of such a function as this when α and β are both monotonic functions of some variable as they are here. In addition, β is a power of α, for, referring to equation (4.2), we see that

$$k_2 = k_2^*(k_1/k_1^*)^{E_2/E_1}$$

or

$$\beta = \rho\alpha^\sigma$$

where

$$\sigma = E_2/E_1 \quad \text{and} \quad \rho = k_2^* k_1^{*-(E_2/E_1)}. \tag{4.8}$$

By that problem we see that, if $\sigma > 1$, $r(c, T)$ has a maximum of

$$R(c) = (E_2 - E_1)\left[\left\{\frac{k_1^*(1 - c)}{E_2}\right\}^{E_2}\left\{\frac{k_2^* c}{E_1}\right\}^{-E_1}\right]^{1/(E_2-E_1)} \tag{4.9}$$

at a temperature

$$T_m(c) = (E_2 - E_1)/R \ln \{E_2 k_2^* c/E_1 k_1^*(1 - c)\}. \tag{4.10}$$

The condition $\sigma = E_2/E_1 > 1$ corresponds to reactions that give out heat. These are called exothermic and may have a maximum reaction rate at some intermediate temperature. Those that absorb heat, the endothermic, have a reaction rate that increases monotonically with temperature. We shall confine our attention to the exothermic case since this is the more interesting. Since $r(c, T)$ has but a single maximum if the value of $T_m(c)$ given by (4.10) falls outside the admissible interval (T_*, T^*), we need only take the nearest bound as is shown in Figure 4.1. If we denote the optimal admissible temperature by $T^0(c)$ then its general variation with c is as shown in Figure 4.2, though in any particular case one bound or the other may not be important. The value of the maximum reaction rate depends on c in the fashion shown in Figure 4.3. There is a discontinuity of curvature in the $R(c)$ curve, but not of slope, at the discontinuities of slope in the $T^0(c)$ curve.

Putting this back into equation (4.6) we see that the decision for T_N can always be made to depend on that for c_N and

$$f_N(c_{N+1}) = \text{Min}\left[\frac{c_N - c_{N+1}}{R(c_N)} + f_{N-1}(c_N)\right], \tag{4.11}$$

where now c_N is the only choice that need be made, and $T_N = T^0(c_N)$.

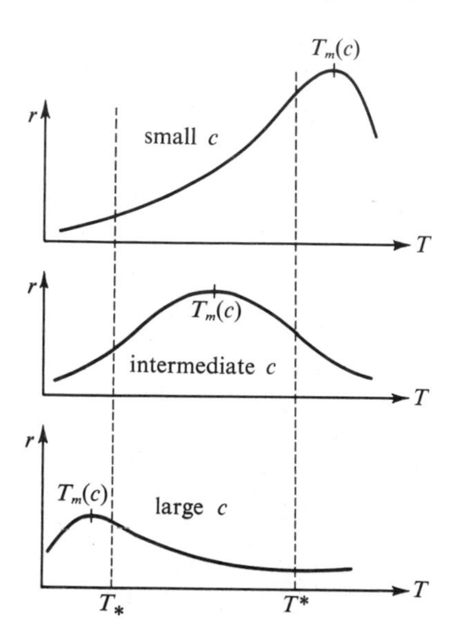

Figure 4.1

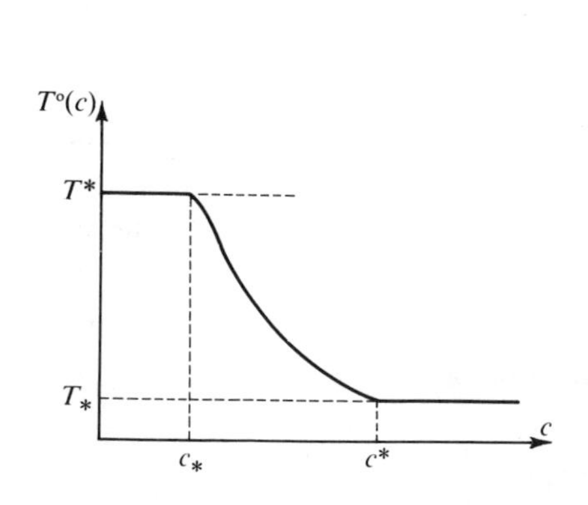

Figure 4.2

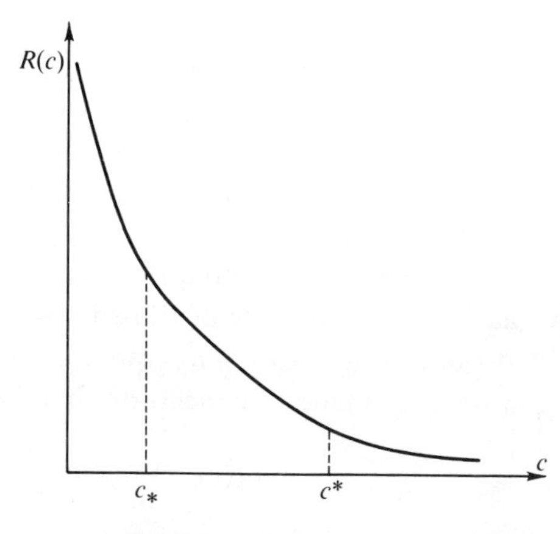

Figure 4.3

4.3. A geometrical interpretation

The first equation of this series has been solved since T_1 must be $T^0(\gamma)$ and

$$f_1(c_2) = \frac{\gamma - c_2}{R(\gamma)}. \tag{4.12}$$

Geometrically considered, the value of $f_1(c_2)$ is the area of the rectangle of base $\gamma - c_2$ and height $1/R(\gamma)$. Now

$$f_2(c_3) = \text{Min}\left[\frac{c_2 - c_3}{R(c_2)} + \frac{\gamma - c_2}{R(\gamma)}\right] \tag{4.13}$$

and an interpretation of the terms on the right is the sum of the areas of the rectangles on the bases (c_3, c_2) and (c_2, γ), of heights $1/R(c_2)$ and $1/R(\gamma)$, respectively. Let us draw this as in Figure 4.4.

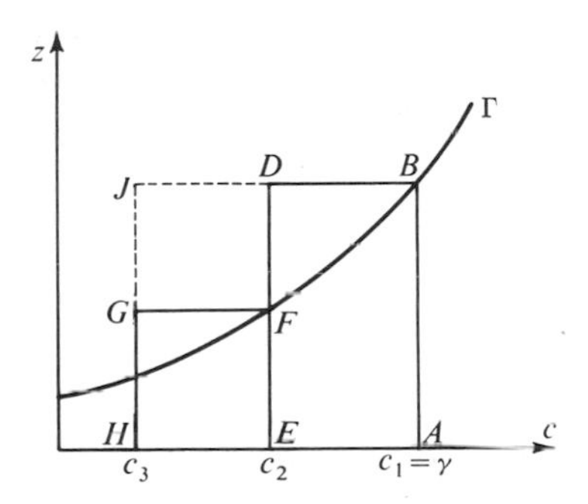

Figure 4.4

In this figure, the curve Γ is the locus $z = 1/R(c)$ which from Figure 4.3 must take the form shown. If we mark the ordinate $c = \gamma$ and draw it up to the curve Γ, then for any c_2 the value of $f_1(c_2)$ is obtained by completing the rectangle $ABDE$ and measuring its area. For the two-stage case, c_3 (the point H) is fixed and for any choice of c_2 the right-hand side of equation (4.13) is the sum of the areas of $ABDE$ and $EFGH$. It is now geometrically obvious that for any c_3 there is a best choice of $c_2(c_3 < c_2 < c_1 = \gamma)$ that minimizes the sum of the areas. For if c_2 is equal to either c_3 or c_1, one or the other of the two stages has been discarded and the required holding time is the area of $ABJH$. But the sum of the holding times for the two stages is less than this by the area of the rectangle $JDFG$. Looking back at the quantity to be minimized in equation (4.13) we see that it is a continuous and differentiable function of c_2 in the interval $c_3 < c_2 < c_1 = \gamma$ and that it has the same value at $c_2 = c_3$ as at $c_2 = c_1$. Hence, by Rolle's theorem, there is a point within the interval

(c_3, c_1) at which its derivative vanishes. The monotonicity and lack of inflection points in Γ assure us that this point will be the unique minimum we require. Denoting dR/dc by $R'(c)$, we see that $c_2^0(c_3)$ satisfies

$$\frac{\partial}{\partial c_2}\left[\frac{c_2 - c_3}{R(c_2)} + \frac{\gamma - c_2}{R(\gamma)}\right] = \left[\frac{1}{R(c_2)} - \frac{R'(c_2)}{R(c_2)}\frac{c_2 - c_3}{R(c_2)} - \frac{1}{R(\gamma)}\right] = 0. \quad (4.14)$$

The easiest way to solve this equation is to rearrange it as

$$c_3 = c_2 - \frac{R^2(c_2)}{R'(c_2)}\left[\frac{1}{R(c_2)} - \frac{1}{R(\gamma)}\right]. \quad (4.15)$$

Thus instead of asking what the c_2 is that is optimal for a given c_3, we find the c_3 for which a given c_2 is optimal, and this can be done by direct calculation. We will not pursue solution of this equation here but will turn first to the graphical presentation of the results.

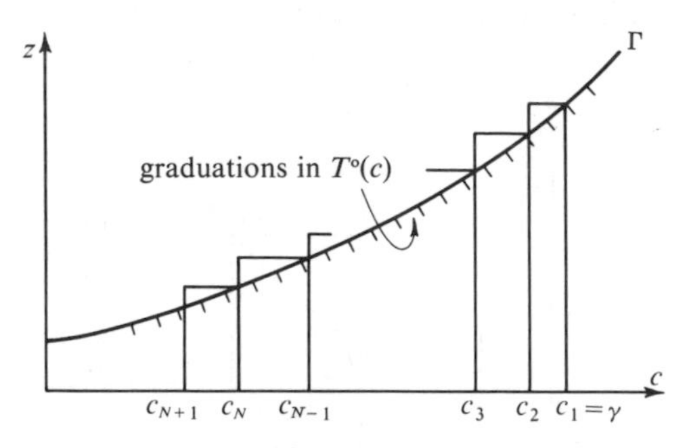

Figure 4.5

The case of N stages can be interpreted in a similar way to the two-stage case. Here we shall be looking for the set of rectangles on the base (c_{N+1}, c_1), with upper right-hand corners on the curve Γ, which have the minimum area. It seems intuitive that as N increases this minimum area should decrease toward the area under the curve Γ, as in Figure 4.5. This idea of minimizing the area under a number of rectangles is closely related to Denbigh's method of maximizing rectangles.*

4.4. A graphical presentation of the results

However the details of the calculation may be carried out it is quite clear that the set of equations (4.11) can be solved with little greater difficulty than in the case of constant temperature. Let us see how the results might be presented graphically instead of in the tabular form of section 3.4.

* See K. G. DENBIGH, "Instantaneous and Overall Reaction Yields," *Chem. Eng. Sci.* **14** (1961), p. 30.

First notice that the optimal choice of temperature is always related to the choice of extent by

$$T_n = T^0(c_n) \tag{4.16}$$

This may be incorporated on a figure of the same type as before by graduating in values of $T^0(c)$ taken from Figure 4.2. Then at the top right-hand corner of the rectangle for stage n we can read off the appropriate temperature as in Figure 4.5.

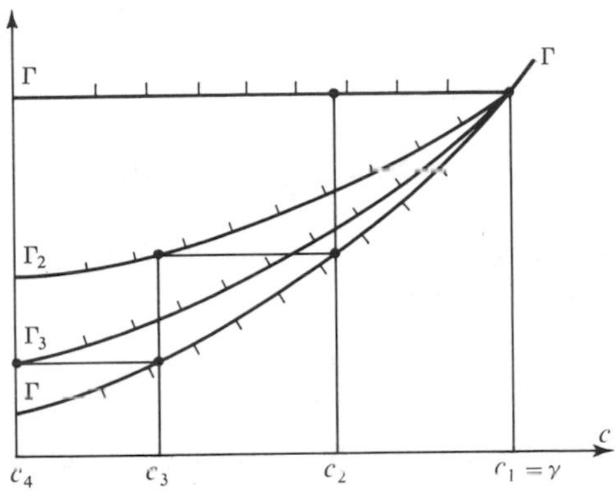

Figure 4.6

Next we notice that the single-stage policy is immediate, for the rectangle $ABDE$ of Figure 4.4 can be drawn immediately. We might formalize this construction by drawing a horizontal line Γ_1 to intersect Γ at $c = \gamma$ as in Figure 4.6. Then given any c_2 the construction for the single stage is to draw a vertical line from $c = c_2$ to Γ_1 and complete the rectangle by drawing a horizontal line to Γ. As a further convenience one might graduate Γ_1 in values of $\theta_1 = f_1(c_3)$ so that this could be read from the top left-hand corner of the rectangle and the optimal temperature T_1 from the right.

Now looking back at Figure 4.4 let us suppose that for the c_2 and c_3 shown, c_2 is indeed $c_2^0(c_3)$. Evidently the point G records this fact without equivocation, for knowing it we could draw the horizontal line to Γ and drop the perpendicular FE to find the appropriate $c_2^0(c_3)$. Now the locus of the point G can be calculated very readily from equation (4.15). For choosing any c_2 ($<\gamma$) this equation gives the abscissa of a point on the locus of G and its ordinate is $1/R(c_2)$. This is the curve Γ_2 in Figure 4.6; it has the parametric equations

$$\begin{aligned} c &= c_2 - \frac{R^2(c_2)}{R'(c_2)}\left\{\frac{1}{R(c_2)} - \frac{1}{R(\gamma)}\right\}, \\ z &= \frac{1}{R(c_2)}, \end{aligned} \tag{4.17}$$

where c_2 is the parameter along it. Denoting the solution of equation (4.14) by $c_2^0(c_3)$ the equation of Γ_2 is

$$z = 1/R[c_2^0(c)]. \tag{4.18}$$

The construction of the optimal policy for two stages is now immediate, for, given c_3, we have only to draw the vertical line $c = c_3$ to Γ_2, a horizontal to Γ, a vertical to Γ_1, and the two rectangles are delineated. If Γ_2 is graduated in $f_2(c_3)$ then at the first corner we read $f_2(c_3) = \theta_1 + \theta_2$, at the second $T_2^0 = T^0[c_2^0(c_3)]$, at the third $\theta_1 = f_1[c_2^0(c_3)]$, and at the final point T_1^0. The holding time for stage 2 is obtained by subtraction: $\theta_2^0 = f_2(c_3) - f_1[c_2^0(c_3)]$.

For the case of three stages we have

$$f_3(c_4) = \text{Min}\left[\frac{c_3 - c_4}{R(c_3)} + f_2(c_3)\right]. \tag{4.19}$$

The optimal choice of c_3 can again be obtained by differentiation and an equation similar to (4.14) results,

$$\frac{1}{R(c_3)} - \frac{R'(c_3)}{R(c_3)}\frac{c_3 - c_4}{R(c_3)} + f_2'(c_3) = 0. \tag{4.20}$$

However this may be solved, it gives the optimal c_3 for any c_4, $c_3^0(c_4)$. This may be used to construct another curve Γ_3, whose equation is

$$z = 1/R[c_3^0(c)], \tag{4.21}$$

and this could be graduated in $f_3(c_4)$. (See Figure 4.6.) Evidently the same construction of verticals and horizontals will quickly lead to the optimal three-stage policy.

The pattern has now been set. At each stage we determine $c_N^0(c_{N+1})$ by the equation

$$\frac{1}{R(c_N)} - \frac{R'(c_N)}{R(c_N)}\frac{c_N - c_{N+1}}{R(c_N)} + f_{N-1}'(c_N) = 0, \tag{4.22}$$

and record the result as a curve

$$\Gamma_N\colon z = 1/R[c_N^0(c)], \tag{4.23}$$

graduated in $f_N(c_{N+1})$. The construction of drawing alternate vertical and horizontal lines from $c = c_{N+1}$ to Γ_N, to Γ, to $\Gamma_{N-1}, \cdots$, to Γ_1, to Γ, then leads immediately to the optimal policy, which can be read from the graduations at the top corners of each rectangle.

4.5. A graphical construction of the solution

The only defect with the preceding construction is that it seems to require a new diagram to be drawn with a new family of curves Γ_n for each γ. However, we notice that Γ_1 can always be drawn since it is a horizontal straight line and immediately begin to wonder if Γ_2 can perhaps be constructed from it. Let us write equation (4.14) for the determination of $c_2^0(c_3)$ in the form

$$\frac{1}{R(c_2)}\left\{1-\frac{c_2R'(c_2)}{R(c_2)}\right\}+c_3\frac{R'(c_2)}{R^2(c_2)}=\frac{1}{R(\gamma)}. \tag{4.24}$$

For any given c_3 we can draw the curve

$$z=\frac{1}{R(c)}\left\{1-\frac{cR'(c)}{R(c)}\right\}+c_3\frac{R'(c)}{R^2(c)}. \tag{4.25}$$

It has the form PQR of Figure 4.7 and meets the curve Γ at $c = c_3$. But the solution of equation (4.24) is Q, the point of intersection of PQR with Γ_1, for here $z = 1/R(\gamma)$. Hence the abscissa of Q is $c_2^0(c_3)$. If, therefore, we drop a vertical from Q to Γ and take a horizontal line US through its intersection with Γ, the point S, vertically above R, must lie on Γ_2. But we might draw several such curves as PQR for various c_3 and so obtain several points on Γ_2.

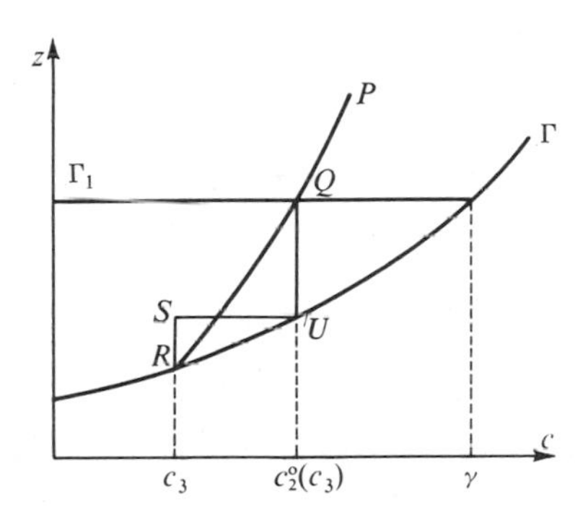

Figure 4.7

If we denote the family of curves such as PQR by $z = h(c; c')$ we may write

$$h(c;c')=\frac{1}{R(c)}\left\{1-\frac{cR'(c)}{R(c)}\right\}+c'\left\{\frac{R'(c)}{R^2(c)}\right\} \tag{4.26}$$

and equation (4.24) becomes

$$h(c_2;c_3)=1/R(c_1).$$

Clearly equation (4.22) can be written in a similar way

$$h(c_N;c_{N+1})=-f'_{N-1}(c_N) \tag{4.27}$$

and the required solution is the intersection of a curve of the h-family with the curve $z = -f'_{N-1}(c)$.

But what is this latter curve? To find this let us recall what $f_N(c_{N+1})$ is; namely,

$$f_N(c_{N+1}) = \text{Min}\left[\frac{c_N - c_{N+1}}{R(c_N)} + \sum_1^{N-1} \frac{c_n - c_{n+1}}{R(c_n)}\right]. \tag{4.28}$$

It has been written this way to show that c_{N+1} only occurs explicitly in the first term, though of course all the other c_n are functions of c_{N+1}, $c_N = c_N^0(c_{N+1})$, etc. If we denote the expression on the right-hand side of this equation by F,

$$f_N'(c_{N+1}) = \frac{df_N}{dc_{N+1}} = \frac{\partial F}{\partial c_{N+1}} + \sum_{n=2}^{N} \frac{\partial F}{\partial c_n}\frac{dc_n}{dc_{N+1}}.$$

But the c_n, $n = 1, \cdots, N$ have been chosen so that F is a minimum, and we have seen that this minimum is an interior stationary point, so all the partial derivatives $\partial F/\partial c_n$ vanish. Hence

$$f_N'(c_{N+1}) = \frac{\partial F}{\partial c_{N+1}} = -\frac{1}{R(c_N)}, \tag{4.29}$$

and c_N is, of course, always the optimal choice $c_N = c_N^0(c_{N+1})$.

It follows by lowering the index N to $N - 1$ that the right-hand side of equation (4.27) is given by a curve

$$z = 1/R[c_{N-1}^0(c_N)]. \tag{4.30}$$

But this is just the curve Γ_{N-1} and so $c_N^0(c_{N+1})$ is given by the intersection of the member of the h-family for c_{N+1} and the curve Γ_{N-1}. The curve Γ_N can therefore be constructed from Γ_{N-1} by precisely the same method as was used to get Γ_2 from Γ_1 and since Γ_1 is immediate all Γ_N can be constructed. Because of the attachments of the h-family to Γ at the points $c = c'$ it is evident that the Γ_N tend to Γ as $N \to \infty$.

The advantage we have gained is that the h-family does not depend on any previously fixed value of the final conversion γ and can be drawn with Γ. Indeed it would seem necessary to tabulate only two functions $g_1(c) = 1/R(c)$ and its derivative $g_2(c) = -R'(c)/R^2(c)$. Then Γ is $z = g_1(c)$ and the h-family $z = g_1(c) + cg_2(c) - c'g_2(c)$.*

The graphical scheme was devised first as a method of presenting the results and it was found that a large amount of information could be condensed on one graph. The structure of the problem and assurance of stationary minima

* See also problem 4 at the end of this chapter for the relation between Γ and the h-family.

was easily obtained from the graphical approach. Its shortcomings, however, led to the examination of the equations and to a graphical method for their solution. In the next section we shall look briefly at the value of this approach in parametric studies.

Finally let us observe that the constructions have employed only straight lines parallel to the axes. We are at liberty, therefore, to distort the scales of z and c in any way we wish to make the curves more suitable to work with.

4.6. Parametric studies

For a given set of parameters k_1^*, k_2^*, E_1, E_2, and γ of the problem, we have seen how to get both an overall picture of the structure of the solution and to calculate its numerical values. In fact we have been at pains to show how to deal with any value of γ. How can we most easily program a set of calculations to cover the whole spectrum of first-order exothermic reversible reactions? The first thing to do is to reduce the number of parameters and this may be done by making all our equations dimensionless.

On page 14 in setting up the original equations we took the total concentration of A and B to be the unit of concentration. Thus the extent variable is already dimensionless being the ratio of the concentration of B to the total concentration. Temperature and holding time are still fully dimensional, however, and to see how to modify them we should look at the expressions we have for them. Equation (4.10) could be written

$$\frac{RT_m(c)}{E_2 - E_1} = \frac{1}{\ln c/(1-c) + \ln (E_2 k_2^*/E_1 k_1^*)}, \tag{4.31}$$

which suggests immediately that we should take as dimensionless temperature

$$t = RT/(E_2 - E_1). \tag{4.32}$$

Let us set the dimensionless ratio

$$\frac{E_2 k_2^*}{E_1 k_1^*} = \kappa, \tag{4.33}$$

then

$$t_m(c) = 1/\{\ln c/(1-c) + \ln \kappa\} \tag{4.34}$$

and the relation between c and the dimensionless optimal temperature involves only one parameter. Figure 4.8 shows $t_m(c)$ as a function of c for various κ. It can be seen that t_m becomes very large when c approaches $1/(1+\kappa)$ from above. In fact even greater economy could be obtained by

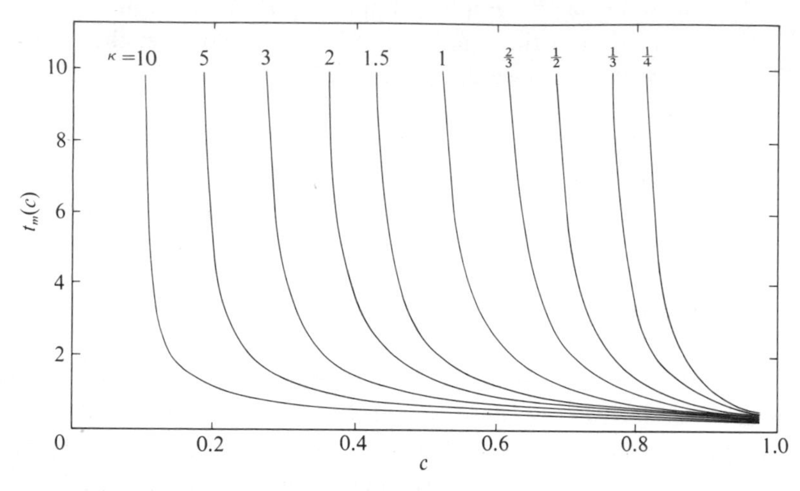

Figure 4.8

plotting $1/t_m(c)$ against c. If the single curve for $\kappa = 1$ were drawn, the curves for various κ could be immediately drawn parallel to it at a distance of ln κ.

Turning to the expression (4.8) for the reaction rate and putting $\sigma = E_2/E_1$, we could write it

$$P(c) = \left[\left(\frac{k_2^*}{E_1}\right)^{E_1}\left(\frac{k_1^*}{E_2}\right)^{-E_2}\right]^{1/(E_2-E_1)} \frac{R(c)}{E_2 - E_1} = \left[\frac{(1-c)^\sigma}{c}\right]^{1/(\sigma-1)} \tag{4.35}$$

where $P(c)$ is the dimensionless reaction rate.

$$P(c) = R(c)/A \tag{4.36}$$

and

$$A = \left\{\frac{k_1^{*\sigma}}{k_2^*}\frac{(\sigma-1)^{\sigma-1}}{\sigma^\sigma}\right\}^{1/(\sigma-1)}. \tag{4.37}$$

The equation of transformation

$$\theta_n = \frac{c_n - c_{n+1}}{R(c_n)}$$

can now be written

$$\psi_n = A\theta_n = \frac{c_n - c_{n+1}}{P(c_n)} \tag{4.38}$$

and evidently ψ_n is a dimensionless holding time. Note that

$$\psi_n = k_1^*\theta_n\left(\frac{\sigma-1}{\sigma}\right)\kappa^{-1/(\sigma-1)}. \tag{4.39}$$

The dimensionless objective function is now $\Sigma_1^N \psi_n$ which has to be minimized subject to $c_1 = \gamma$. If

$$\varphi_N(c_{N+1}) = \text{Min} \sum_1^N \psi_n,$$

then

$$\varphi_N(c_{N+1}) = Af_N(c_{N+1}). \tag{4.40}$$

For the graphical construction we need Γ which is now $z = 1/P(c) = g(c)$ and the h-family $z = g_1(c) + cg_2(c) - c'g_2(c)$. Now

$$g_1(c) = \{c/(1-c)^\sigma\}^{1/(\sigma-1)}, \tag{4.41}$$

$$g_2(c) = \frac{g_1(c)}{\sigma - 1}\left[\frac{1}{c} + \frac{\sigma}{1-c}\right]. \tag{4.42}$$

Figures 4.9 and 4.10 show the functions $g_1(c)$ and $g_2(c)$ for various σ.

It is interesting to observe that two dimensionless parameters, κ and σ, have been left, the others having been absorbed in making the variables dimensionless. Even more significant is the fact that they are separated and κ appears alone in the optimal temperature relation whereas σ appears alone in g_1 and g_2. This means that we nowhere have the need for a two-parameter family of curves and a complete parametric study can be built up from the three Figures 4.8, 4.9, and 4.10.

Actually we have glossed over one important fact in this analysis, namely that the bounds T_* and T^* should also be included among the parameters. Now T^* will certainly be important if the feed is anything like pure A, for Figure 4.8 shows how t_m goes to infinity. However, given T^*, this figure shows the value of c below which the temperature must be held at its upper bound. $R(c)$ will not, of course, have the same form as in equation (4.35) beyond this point but it can be made dimensionless with the same parameter A. The details are left as an exercise to the reader.

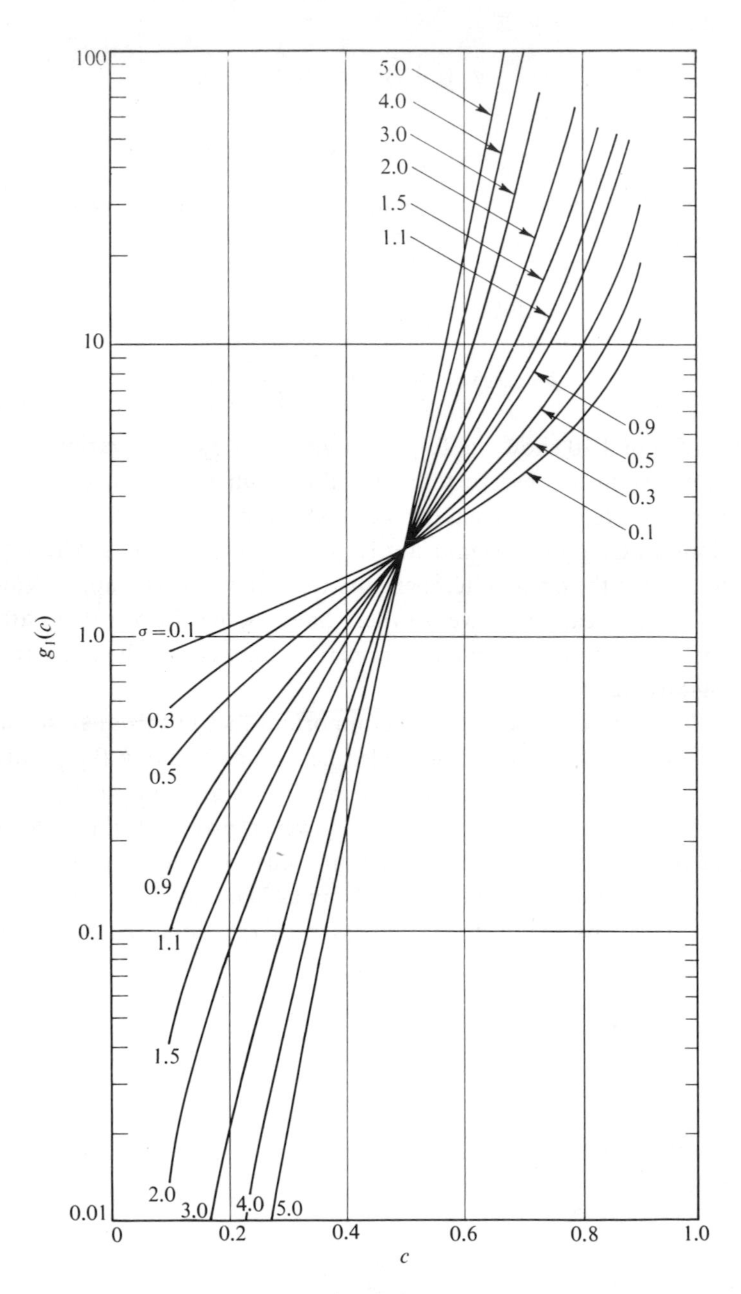
100
10
1.0
0.1
0.01
$g_1(c)$
0
0.2
0.4
0.6
0.8
1.0
c
5.0
4.0
3.0
2.0
1.5
1.1
0.9
0.5
0.3
0.1
σ = 0.1
0.3
0.5
0.9
1.1
1.5
2.0
3.0
4.0
5.0

Figure 4.9

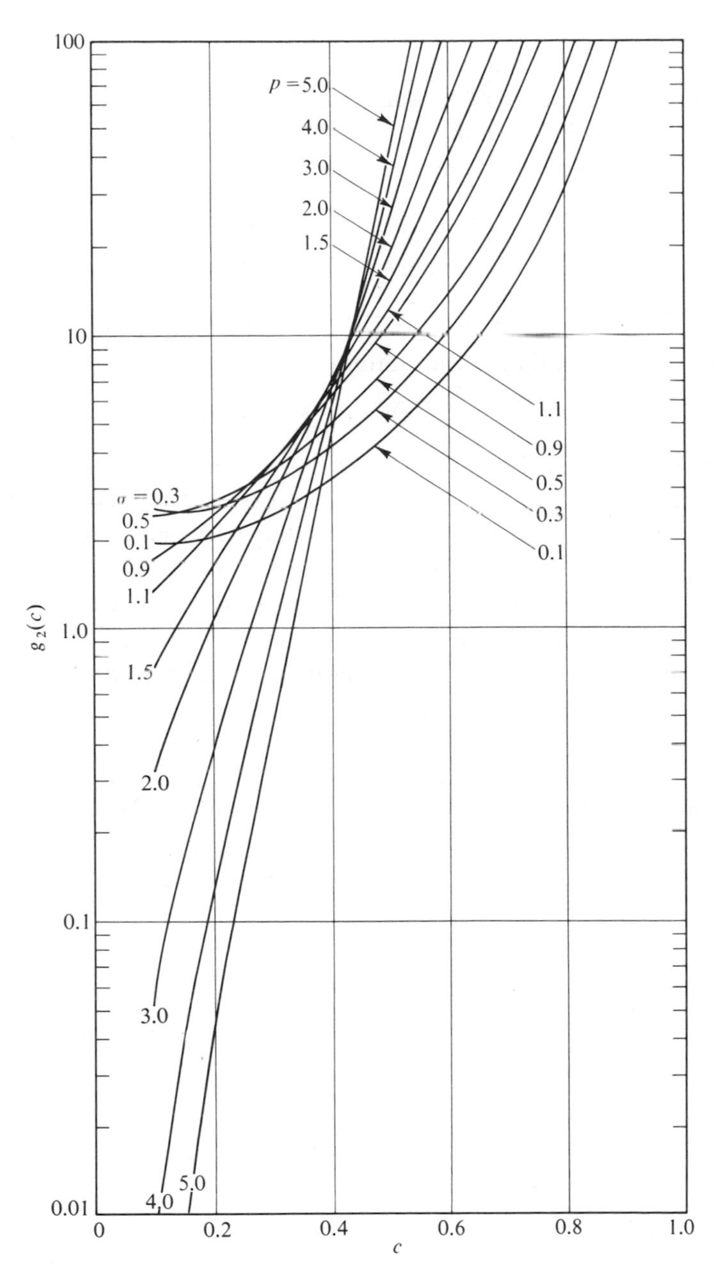
100
10
1.0
0.1
0.01
$g_2(c)$
0
0.2
0.4
0.6
0.8
1.0
c
p = 5.0
4.0
3.0
2.0
1.5
1.1
0.9
0.5
0.3
0.1
σ = 0.3
0.5
0.1
0.9
1.1
1.5
2.0
3.0
4.0
5.0

Figure 4.10

Problems

1. Carry out the details of making $r(c, T^*)$ dimensionless and derive the functions g_1 and g_2 for this.
2. Show by geometrical arguments that
$$f'_N(c_{N+1}) = -1/R[c_N^0(c_{N+1})].$$
3. Consider the situation with the so-called second-order reaction,
$$r(c, T) = k_1(a - c)(b - c) - k_2c^2.$$
4. Interpret the equation of the h-family
$$z = g_1(c) + (c - c')g_2(c)$$
geometrically and show how it is possible to construct this family graphically from a knowledge of $g_1(c)$ (that is, Γ) alone. Comment on the accuracy of this construction and the relevance of the remark on changes of scale at the end of section 4.5.
5. Show how to find the maximum of $\alpha A - \beta B$ where α and β are both monotonic functions of a decision variable. If $\beta = \rho\alpha^\sigma$ show that the maximum occurs when $\alpha^{\sigma-1} = (A/\rho\sigma B)$ and is of magnitude
$$\left[\frac{(\sigma - 1)^{\sigma-1}}{\sigma^\sigma}\frac{A^\sigma}{\rho B}\right]^{1/(\sigma-1)}.$$
6. Letting $\tau = 1/(\sigma - 1)$, show that the maximum can also be written
$$\left(\frac{A}{1 + \tau}\right)^{1+\tau} \bigg/ \left(\frac{\rho B}{\tau}\right)^\tau.$$

CHAPTER 5

Related problems and Lagrange multipliers

We shall continue in this chapter to use the example of the sequence of stirred reactors to illustrate some further points.

5.1. Dual problems

In the problems on the sequence of reactors, Ia (also, IIa) was formulated as follows. Certain decisions had to be made so that for a given conversion from c_{N+1} to c_1 the total holding time $\Theta = \Sigma\, \theta_n$ was minimum. In the corresponding problems Ic (and IIc) the same decisions had to be taken but this

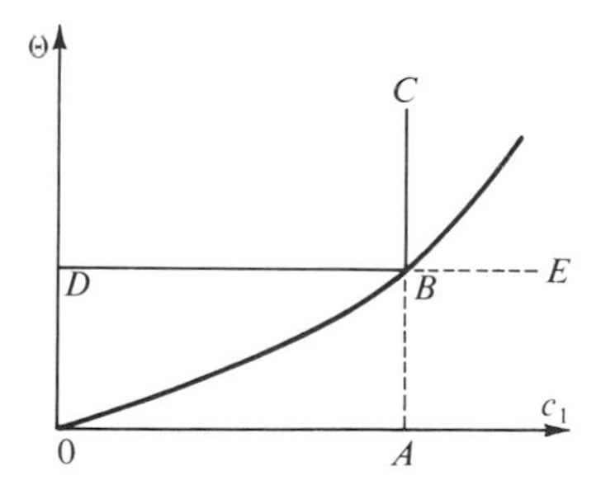

Figure 5.1

time the total holding time $\Theta = \Sigma\, \theta_n$ was given and the conversion had to be maximized. These two problems illustrate the mathematical relationship of duality; if one problem is called the *primal*, the other is called its *dual*. We want to show that the solution of one provides the solution of the other.

Suppose then that we regard N and c_{N+1} as fixed and consider problem Ia (or IIa). If we solve this for a variety of values of c_1 we might plot the resulting minimum of Θ against c_1 and obtain such a figure as Figure 5.1. The curve in this region is really a boundary between possible and impossible working conditions. Thus suppose we fix on a particular c_1 as at the point A, B is the minimum value of the total holding time, and no value on AB is attainable with an admissible operating or design policy. On the other hand, there are many other suboptimal policies of operation that would result in a larger total holding time than the minimum, and so a point on BC represents a possible design of the system. Evidently then conditions above the line are possible and those below the line impossible. Consider now the horizontal line DBE: this is of constant total holding time Θ, and evidently conversions on DB are attainable since they correspond to possible, though suboptimal, operations. On the other hand, a conversion on BE is not attainable with the given Θ. It follows that B, the maximum conversion attainable with this Θ (that is, the solution of problem Ic), lies on the curve defined by the solution of problem Ia. Since there is a definite optimal operating policy associated with every point such as B on the curve, this optimal policy solves both the primal and dual problems. The boundary between the possible and the impossible must be unique.

5.2. The Lagrange multiplier

Consider now the problems Ib and IIb. Here the decision policy was to be made so as to maximize $(c_1 - c_{N+1}) - \lambda\Sigma\,\theta_n$. It was not necessary to put any limitation on $\Sigma\,\theta_n = \Theta$ since if θ_n were made too large the objective function would be negative. Again consider N and c_{N+1} fixed; then we claim that the solution must again correspond to a point on the boundary curve OB of Figure 5.1. It certainly cannot correspond to a point below the curve since these conditions are unattainable. If the solution of problem Ib (or IIb) corresponded to a point above OB, say on the line DB, then we could increase the objective function by moving to the point B (since this would increase c_1 without altering Θ) and the original solution would not be optimal.

The precise point on the boundary that gives the solution will of course depend on λ. We would expect the point to move down the curve to 0 as λ increases. The number λ is called a Lagrange multiplier and can be introduced in a similar way in many problems converting a problem with restrictions into an unrestricted one. When this problem is solved the value of λ must then be found to satisfy the restrictions.

To use problem Ib (or IIb) to solve the other two problems we would proceed as follows. Let

$$g_{N,\lambda}(c_{N+1}) = \text{Max} \sum_{1}^{N} \{c_n - c_{n+1} - \lambda\theta_n\}, \tag{5.1}$$

then, by the principle of optimality,

$$g_{N,\lambda}(c_{N+1}) = \text{Max} \sum_{1}^{N} \{c_N - c_{N+1} - \lambda\theta_N + g_{N-1,\lambda}(c_N)\}, \tag{5.2}$$

with the usual starting equation $g_{0,\lambda} = 0$. These equations can be solved for any λ and give the complete N-stage policy as a function of c_{N+1}. Now repeat this for several values of λ and from the results for given c_{N+1} extract the values of c_1 that are attained with the optimal policy. These will give such a

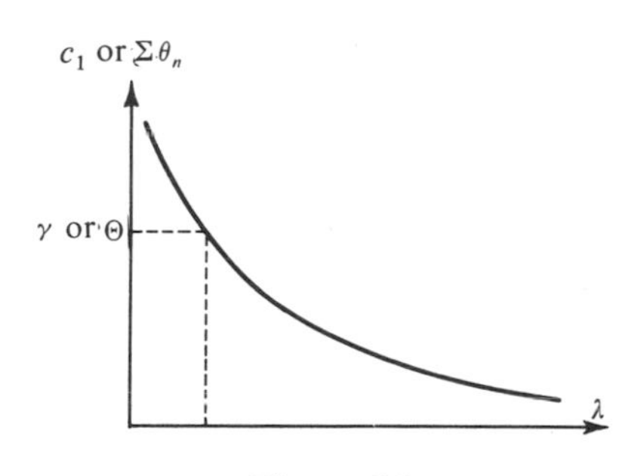

Figure 5.2

curve as Figure 5.2. The solution of problem Ia (or IIa) is given by the value of λ for which $c_1 = \gamma$. This gives a definite value of λ and the policy given by the solution of problem b for this λ is the solution of problem a for that γ.

Similarly if $\Sigma\,\theta_n$ is plotted against λ, for fixed c_{N+1} and N, we shall have just such a figure as before. The solution of problem Ic (or IIc) then comes from the choice of λ that just gives $\Sigma\,\theta_n = \Theta$. Here an economy has been effected since we saw that to formulate this problem correctly we had to use two state variables which brought on a mild attack of dimensionality. Problem b, however, involves only one state variable and it makes less demand on machine storage to repeat the solution of this problem for several λ than to solve problem c. This will be formalized in section 5.4.

5.3. The economic interpretation of the Lagrange multiplier

In the construction of the objective function $(c_1 - c_{N+1}) - \lambda\,\Sigma_1^N\,\theta_n$ we are really making an elementary economic statement. If the unit of money is taken to be the value of a unit increase in c, then λ is the cost of a unit of θ in this monetary scale. The objective function is thus the net profit or difference between the increased value of the product and the cost of holding time. As the cost of holding time, λ, goes up, we should expect the total holding time that it is economic to employ would go down.

If we have both an estimate of λ from economic considerations and a restriction on the total holding time, then the diagram is capable of a further interpretation. In Figure 5.3, the optimal $\Sigma\,\theta_n$ is plotted against λ. Suppose that the estimated λ and restriction on Θ give a point A. Evidently if there were only a restriction on Θ the value of λ we should take to solve the problem would correspond to D, a rather smaller value than at the point A. This means that the restriction on holding time is really no limitation. The real limitation comes about because of the high cost, λ, of the holding time. At this price we

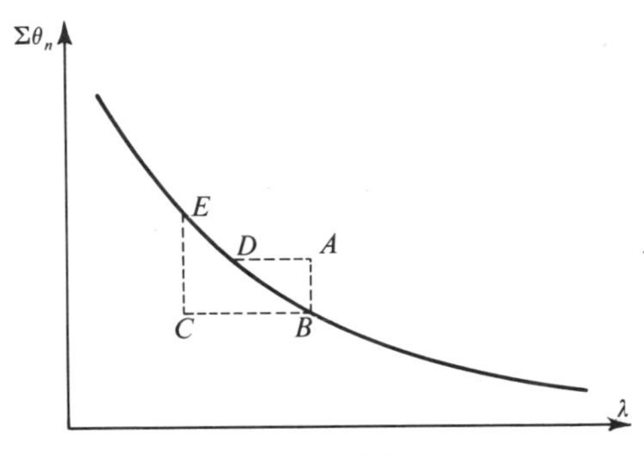

Figure 5.3

cannot afford to use all the available holding time but must work at a point B which gives the greatest holding time that it is economical to use. Conversely, if the estimates of both λ and Θ give a point like C, the restriction on holding time is the real limitation for at this cost it would have been economical to use more (the point E). However, because of the restriction, we must work at the point B and here the holding time has acquired a scarcity value λ greater than its real value.

5.4. The formal application of the Lagrange multiplier

The way in which state variables can be traded with restrictions is illustrated in the following example. Suppose we wish to maximize a sum of N functions, $\Sigma_1^N\, g_n(x_n)$, of the n positive variables $x_1, \cdots, x_N$, but the choice of the x_n is restricted by a number of conditions, such as

$$\sum_{p=1}^{N} h_{mp}(x_p) \leqslant k_m, \qquad m = 1, \cdots, M. \tag{5.3}$$

Then evidently the maximum we obtain will be governed by the set of quantities k_m and we must write

$$\text{Max} \sum_1^N g_n(x_n) = f_N(k_1, \cdots, k_M). \tag{5.4}$$

Now suppose we make an allocation x_N. The remaining allocations $x_{N-1}, \cdots, x_1$ have to be made subject to

$$\sum_{p=1}^{N-1} h_{mp}(x_p) \leqslant k_m - h_{mN}(x_N). \tag{5.5}$$

The maximum of $\Sigma_1^{N-1} g_n(x_n)$ subject to these restrictions is $f_{N-1}[k_1 - h_{1N}(x_N), \cdots, k_M - h_{MN}(x_N)]$. Thus writing $\Sigma_1^N g_n(x_n)$ as $g_N(x_N) + \Sigma_1^{N-1} g_n(x_n)$ and applying the principle of optimality we have

$$f_N(k_1, \cdots, k_M) = \underset{x_N}{\text{Max}} [g_N(x_N) + f_{N-1}\{k_1 - h_{1N}(x_N), \cdots, k_M - h_{MN}(x_N)\}]. \tag{5.6}$$

This is a straight-forward dynamic programming problem but its dimensionality is M and the storage requirements, as we have seen, depend exponentially on M. However, if we modify the objective function to

$$\sum_1^N g_n(x_n) - \lambda_M \sum_1^N h_{Mn}(x_n), \tag{5.7}$$

we can solve this problem for fixed λ_M and consider only the first $(M - 1)$ of the restrictions (5.3). Thus we can write

$$f_N(k_1, \cdots, k_{M-1}; \lambda_M) = \text{Max} \sum_1^N \{g_n(x_n) - \lambda_M h_{Mn}(x_n)\}, \tag{5.8}$$

and the dimensionality of this is only $(M - 1)$. When it has been solved, we shall have to search for the λ_M that just satisfies the last condition.

In general we might trade $(M - L)$ of the restrictions off for Lagrange multipliers and write

$$f_N(k_1, \cdots, k_L; \lambda_{L+1}, \cdots, \lambda_M) = \text{Max} \sum_1^N \left\{g_n(x_n) - \sum_{L+1}^M \lambda_m h_{mn}(x_n)\right\}. \tag{5.9}$$

We now have a problem with dimensionality L but must look for the set of $(M - L)$ Lagrange multipliers that satisfies the last $(M - L)$ of the restrictions. This is in effect trading off computer memory for time.

5.5. Linear programming

If the functions g and h in the preceding example are linear we have a standard linear programming problem. Thus we may ask for the maximum of $\Sigma_{n=1}^{N} c_n x_n$, where

$$\sum_{p=1}^{N} a_{mp} x_p \leqslant b_m, \qquad m = 1, \cdots, M \tag{5.10}$$

and

$$x_p \geqslant 0, \qquad p = 1, \cdots, N. \tag{5.11}$$

This maximum will be a function of the b's and we write

$$f_N(b_1, \cdots, b_M) = \text{Max} \sum^{N} c_n x_n. \tag{5.12}$$

The application of the principal of optimality as above now gives

$$f_N(b_1, \cdots, b_M) = \text{Max}\,\{c_N x_N + f_{N-1}(b_1 - a_{1N} x_N, \cdots, b_M - a_{MN} x_N)\}, \tag{5.13}$$

subject to $x_N \geqslant 0$.

Now

$$f_1(b_1, \cdots, b_M) = c_1 \,\underset{m}{\text{Max}}\, (b_m / a_{m1})$$

if the a_{mn}, b_m, and c_n are all positive. It is at a point where at least one of the inequalities (5.10) is an equality. Equation (5.13) then gives

$$f_2(b_1, \cdots, b_M) = \underset{x_2}{\text{Max}} \left[c_2 x_2 + c_1 \,\underset{m}{\text{Max}}\, (b_m - a_{m2} x_2)/a_{m1} \right] \tag{5.14}$$

and again the choice of x_2 must lie on the boundary of the region where at least one inequality is an equality. In this way the linear program could be solved, though as a computational algorithm it is greatly inferior to the simplex technique.

If in the Lagrange multiplier formulation we let $L = M$, then equation (5.9) gives

$$f_N(\lambda_1, \cdots, \lambda_M) = \text{Max} \sum_{n=1}^{N} \left\{ c_n - \sum_{m=1}^{M} \lambda_m a_{mn} \right\} x_n. \tag{5.15}$$

Now if the coefficients in this new linear combination of x_n are positive, the maximum will correspond to a choice of λ_m that makes the negative part of (5.15) as small as possible, that is, to a choice of λ_m that minimizes $\Sigma_1^M \lambda_m b_m$ subject to $\Sigma_1^M \lambda_m a_{mn} \leqslant c_n$. This is the dual linear programming problem and shows an interesting connection between Lagrange multipliers and duality.

Bibliography

The reduction of dimensionality by the use of a Lagrange multiplier is discussed in detail in BELLMAN, *Applied Dynamic Programming* (Bibliography 1.8); see Chapter 2 in particular.

5.4. The formal application of this section is taken from:

BELLMAN, R., "Dynamic Programming and Lagrange Multipliers," *Proc. Nat. Acad. Sci. U.S.*, **42** (1956), 767.

5.5. For the relation to linear programming see also:

VADJA, S., *Mathematical Programming* (Bibliography 1.6).

Problem 2 is taken from

ZENER, C., "Mathematical Aid in Optimizing Engineering Designs," *Proc. Nat. Acad. Sci. U.S.*, **47** (1961), 537.

See also BELLMAN, *Applied Dynamic Programming* (Bibliography 1.8), Appendix II, by S. DREYFUS and M. FREIMER, for a discussion of duality in mathematical programming.

Problems

1. Consider the maximization of the geometric mean of N quantities with fixed arithmetic mean and its dual in the style of problems a, b, and c.
2. If

$$C(x_1, \cdots, x_N) = \sum_{1}^{N-1} T_i,$$

where

$$T_i = a_i \prod_{j=1}^{N} x_j^{b_{ij}}$$

show that the minimum value of C is $K \Pi_1^{N+1} \alpha_i^{-\alpha_i}$ where α_i, $i = 1, \cdots, N+1$, is the set of numbers making $\Pi_{j=1}^{N-1} T_j^{-\alpha_j}$ a constant κ independent of the x.

3. To fix ideas on the linear programming example, work the following problem and its dual in full. Maximize $4x_1 + 3x_2$, subject to $x_1 \geqslant 0$, $x_2 \geqslant 0$, $x_1 + 2x_2 \leqslant 4$, $6x_1 + x_2 \leqslant 6$.

CHAPTER 6

Some problems in economics

Much of the early development of dynamic programming was stimulated by economic problems. From the didactic point of view, however, these are perhaps a less satisfactory topic to begin with, since the mathematical models of economics are much more open to question than those of engineering science. In this chapter we shall discuss rather briefly one or two problems of allocation and control, not with any intention of developing economic theory but merely to show how the dynamic programming technique can be applied. Most of these problems have been examined quite fully in published results elsewhere and we shall try to provide at least some entrée into the field. At the same time we shall have occasion to notice some of the ways of overcoming difficulties that are common to problems in many areas. It should be said that a rather wide interpretation of the term "economics" has been taken and it is hoped that the note of levity in the formulation of some of the problems will neither offend the serious-minded reader nor blind him to the much wider application of the methods.

6.1. Bottleneck problems

This name was coined by Bellman for situations in which some restriction is present and the optimal policy involves the alleviation of this restriction at the expense of short-term advantages. We consider a situation in which the production of a commodity A requires the raw material B. The reserves of this raw material are maintained by a process of self-reproduction in a system C. The capacity of the reproductive system is limited however, and, to enlarge it further, quantities of B must be consumed. This is the bottleneck and if the objective is to maximize the production of A over a period of N years, it may well be best not to make any A at first but to devote all the resource of B to self-reproduction and enlargement of the bottleneck. With a piety proper in the affluent society A has sometimes been conceived to be automobiles and B steel, but we are concerned here with the general situation and will dispense with this picturesqueness. The existence of this lag phase in which the situation is being adapted for future productivity is highly suggestive in fields far removed from economics. Its bearing on problems of bacterial growth is currently being investigated.

To arrive at a set of equations let us set a definite period over which the production of A is to be maximized and divide the period into N intervals, numbering them from the end to the beginning as usual. (See Table 6.1.) Let x_{n+1} be the amount of B available at the beginning of the interval n, y_{n+1} the

Table 6.1

	N	$\cdots n+1$	n	$n-1 \cdots 2$	1
Supply of B	x_{N+1} x_N $\cdots$	$\cdots$ x_{n+1}	x_n $\cdots$	$\cdots$ x_2	x_1
(Allocation to reproduction)	y_{N+1} y_N	y_{n+1}	y_n	y_2	
(Allocation to increase capacity)	z_{N+1} z_N	z_{n+1}	z_n	z_2	

amount used to reproduce itself, and z_{n+1} the amount devoted to alleviating the bottleneck restriction during the interval n. This restriction is represented by saying that y_{n+1} cannot exceed the current capacity c_{n+1},

$$y_{n+1} \leqslant c_{n+1}. \tag{6.1}$$

The alleviation of the restriction is represented by supposing that c_{n+1} is increased by βz_{n+1} when an amount z_{n+1} is allocated to this purpose. Thus the capacity c_n at the end of interval n is

$$c_n = c_{n+1} + \beta z_{n+1}. \tag{6.2}$$

The reproduction of B can be represented by saying that the amount available at the end of the period is $(1 + \alpha)$ times the allocation y_{n+1}, $(\alpha > 0)$,

$$x_n = (1 + \alpha) y_{n+1}. \tag{6.3}$$

It is assumed that all the B that is not allocated to reproduction or to increasing the capacity is used for the production of A. Thus the total production of A is

$$0 = \sum_{1}^{N} (x_{n+1} - y_{n+1} - z_{n+1}), \tag{6.4}$$

and this has to be maximized.

Summarizing the problem in the standard form of Chapter 2, we have:

(i) State: x_n, c_n.

(ii) Decision: y_n, z_n.

(iii) Transformation: $x_n = (1 + \alpha)y_{n+1}, \quad y_{n+1} \leqslant c_{n+1},$
$c_n = c_{n+1} + \beta z_{n+1}.$

(iv) Constraints: $y_n \geqslant 0$, $z_n \geqslant 0$, $y_n + z_n \leqslant x_n$.

(v) Objective function: Maximize $\Sigma_1^N(x_{n+1} - y_{n+1} - z_{n+1})$.

(vi) Parameters: α, β.

The amount of B available at the beginning of the process is x_{N+1}, and the existing capacity for reproduction is c_{N+1}; the maximum of the objective function depends on these. We therefore write

$$f_N(x_{N+1}, c_{N+1}) = \text{Max} \sum_1^N (x_{n+1} - y_{n+1} - z_{n+1}). \tag{6.5}$$

Now applying the principle of optimality we see that the initial decision (y_{N+1}, z_{N+1}) must be followed by the optimal policy for the remaining $(N - 1)$ stages with respect to the resulting state (x_N, c_N). Thus

$$f_N(x_{N+1}, c_{N+1}) = \text{Max}\,[x_{N+1} - y_{N+1} - z_{N+1} + f_{N-1}(x_N, c_N)], \tag{6.6}$$

the maximization being by choice of y_{N+1} and z_{N+1} and the transformation given by equations (6.1) through (6.3).

The solution of these equations starts with the platitude that $f_0 \equiv 0$ and hence

$$f_1(x_2, c_2) = x_2, \tag{6.7}$$

the policy being $y_2 = z_2 = 0$. This merely says that at the end of the period all the available supply of B should be devoted to the production of A. For the penultimate interval we have

$$f_2(x_3, c_3) = \text{Max}\,[x_3 - y_3 - z_3 + x_2]. \tag{6.8}$$

By virtue of (6.3) the quantity to be maximized is

$$x_3 + \alpha y_3 - z_3. \tag{6.9}$$

This means that y_3 should be made as large as possible and z_3 kept at zero. If $z_3 = 0$ the two restraints on y_3 are

$$y_3 \leqslant c_3, \qquad y_3 \leqslant x_3.$$

Thus, if

$$x_3 \leqslant c_3, \qquad y_3 = x_3, \qquad f_2(x_3, c_3) = (1 + \alpha)x_3$$

and if

$$x_3 \geqslant c_3, \qquad y_3 = c_3, \qquad f_2(x_3, c_3) = x_3 + \alpha c_3,$$

or

$$f_2(x_3, c_3) = x_3 + \alpha \min (x_3, c_3). \tag{6.10}$$

We could go on like this building up formulas of greater and greater complexity, but let us back off and see certain general features. Firstly, we notice that the formulas being built up are linear in x_{N+1} and c_{N+1}, and since

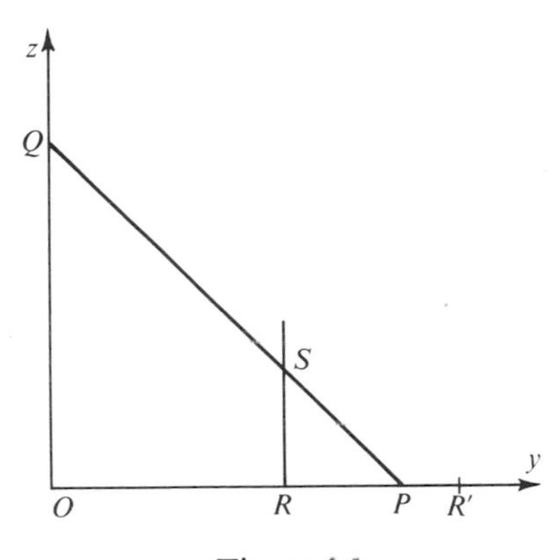

Figure 6.1

all the equations are linear this linearity must persist. Secondly, because of this linearity the policy is always an extreme one. To see the reason for this let us consider the policy plane with coordinates y and z as in Figure 6.1. (We may drop the suffix n for the moment.) The requirement that y and z be positive means that the point representing the policy is restricted to the first quadrant. But also $x - y - z$ must not be negative so that (y, z) must lie in the triangle OPQ where the length of OP and OQ is x. If $c \leqslant x$ the restriction on capacity $y \leqslant c$ is a vertical line RS and the area of admissible policies is further reduced to the trapezoid $ORSQ$. If $c > x$ the point R', $y = c$ lies outside the triangle and capacity is no real restriction. A policy on the line PQ means that no B is allocated to the production of A. Now the quantity to be maximized must, as we have seen, be linear since it starts that way and all the equations are linear. If therefore it were represented as a surface above the y, z plane, it would itself be a plane sloping up in some direction. To find the maximum we would therefore go as far as possible in this direction and this would necessarily lead to a vertex of the admissible region. For example, the contours of the expression (6.9) that had to be maximized are shown as broken lines in Figure 6.2, and the arrow shows the direction of steepest ascent. Evidently R (that is, $y = c, z = 0$) represents the attainable maximum when $c < x$, and P when $c \geqslant x$. In fact we can lay down very simple rules for

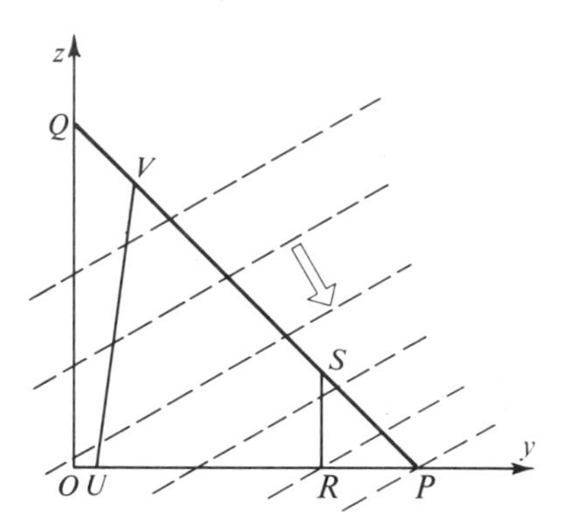

Figure 6.2

finding the maximum of a linear expression $L + My + Nz$. They are listed in Table 6.2. The policy corresponding to Q is not realistic since it would ter-

Table 6.2

M	*N*	*M/N*	*Policy*
negative	negative	—	O: $y = z = 0$
positive	negative	—	R: $y = c, z = 0$ if $c < x$
			P: $y = x, z = 0$ if $x < c$
positive	positive	>1	S: $y = c, z = x - c$ if $c < x$
			P: $y = x, z = 0$ if $x < c$

minate the process, exhausting the supply of B by using it all for increased capacity. We should feel that it is wasteful to increase the capacity beyond the amount of B available for reproduction at the end of the interval, and therefore that $c + \beta z \leqslant (1 + \alpha)y$. This condition, $(1 + \alpha)y - \beta z \geqslant c$ would bound the admissible policy away from the axis OQ by a line such as UV and would insure that the apparently optimal policy was not self destructive. Another condition that has been applied in this problem is that no more than a certain fraction of the supply of B should be used for the production of A, and this bounds the admissible region away from the origin by a line $y + z = (1 - \epsilon)x$. It is a way of preventing self-destruction by $y = z = 0$ and avoids the finality of using the total resource in the last step; we shall not however invoke it here. The linearity of the problem thus introduces a very valuable feature in the search for the maximum since it requires only the examination of a finite number of vertices. However it also enables a valuable reduction in dimensionality which we must now examine.

6.2. Reduction in dimensionality

Since the equations are linear and the maximum of the objective function is a linear homogeneous expression in x_{N+1} and c_{N+1} we can work entirely in the ratios of quantities. Thus setting

$$\gamma_n = c_n/x_n, \tag{6.11}$$

$$f_N(x_{N+1}, c_{N+1}) = x_{N+1}\varphi_N(\gamma_{N+1}), \tag{6.12}$$

and

$$\xi_n = x_n/x_{n+1}, \qquad \eta_n = y_n/x_n, \qquad \zeta_n = z_n/x_n, \tag{6.13}$$

we may translate the equations of the previous section. Equation (6.1) becomes

$$\eta_{n+1} \leqslant \gamma_{n+1}. \tag{6.14}$$

The reproduction of *B*, equation (6.2) is

$$\xi_n = (1 + \alpha)\eta_{n+1}, \tag{6.15}$$

and the growth of capacity

$$\begin{aligned} \gamma_n &= (\gamma_{n+1} + \beta\zeta_{n+1})/\xi_n \\ &= (\gamma_{n+1} + \beta\zeta_{n+1})/(1 + \alpha)\eta_{n+1}. \end{aligned} \tag{6.16}$$

The restrictions also imply that

$$\eta_n \geqslant 0, \qquad \zeta_n \geqslant 0, \qquad \eta_n + \zeta_n \leqslant 1. \tag{6.17}$$

Dividing equation (6.6) by z_{N+1} and using (6.12) we have

$$\begin{aligned} \varphi_N(\gamma_{N+1}) &= \text{Max}\,[1 - \eta_{N+1} - \zeta_{N+1} + \xi_N\varphi_{N-1}(\gamma_N)] \\ &= \text{Max}\,[1 - \eta_{N+1} - \zeta_{N+1} + (1 + \alpha)\eta_{N+1}\varphi_{N-1}(\gamma_N)]. \end{aligned} \tag{6.18}$$

Apart from the reduction of dimensionality in the state variables a minor advantage has been gained in the policy space. In such diagrams as Figures 6.1 and 6.2, the boundaries *PQ* and *RS* would both vary from stage to stage, but by the reduction of dimensionality the boundary *PQ* in Figure 6.3 is a fixed one, $\eta + \zeta = 1$, and only the boundary *RS*, $\eta = \gamma$, moves from stage to stage.

Since we know that φ_N is going to be linear let us set

$$\varphi_N(\gamma_{N+1}) = A_N + B_N\gamma_{N+1}. \tag{6.19}$$

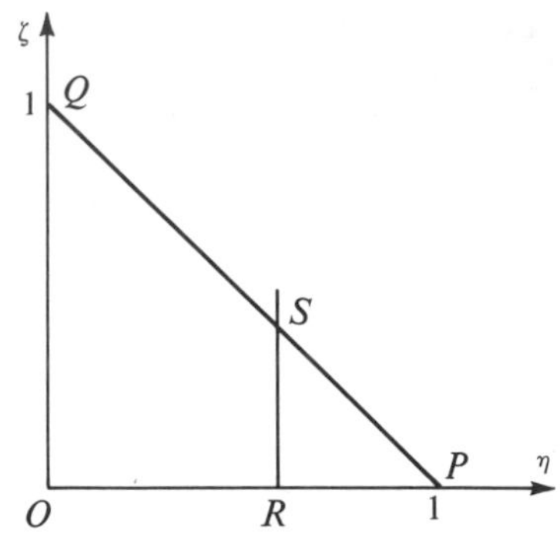

Figure 6.3

Then substituting into equation (6.18) gives

$$\begin{aligned} A_N + B_N\gamma_{N+1} &= \text{Max}\,[1 - \eta_{N+1} - \zeta_{N+1} + \xi_N(A_{N-1} + B_{N-1}\gamma_N)] \\ &= \text{Max}\,[1 - \eta_{N+1} - \zeta_{N+1} + A_{N-1}(1+\alpha)\eta_{N+1} \\ &\qquad + B_{N-1}(\gamma_{N+1} + \beta\zeta_{N+1})] \\ &= \text{Max}\,[(1 + B_{N-1}\gamma_{N+1}) + \{(1+\alpha)A_{N-1} - 1\}\eta_{N+1} \\ &\qquad + \{\beta B_{N-1} - 1\}\zeta_{N+1}]. \end{aligned} \tag{6.20}$$

This allows us to write down all the possibilities for the optimal policy and transformation of A_n and B_n going from stage, as in Table 6.3. Let us prove

Table 6.3

	Conditions		
	$(1+\alpha)A_{N-1} - 1$	$\beta B_{N-1} - 1$	$\gamma_{N+1} - 1$
(i)	negative	negative	
(ii)	positive	negative	negative
(iii)	positive	negative	positive
(iv)	positive	positive	negative
(v)	positive	positive	positive

	Policy			*Transformation*	
		η_{N+1}	ζ_{N+1}	A_N	B_N
(i)	O	0	0	1	B_{N-1}
(ii)	R	γ_{N+1}	0	1	$(1+\alpha)A_{N-1} + B_{N-1} - 1$
(iii)	P	1	0	$(1+\alpha)A_{N-1}$	B_{N-1}
(iv)	S	γ_{N+1}	$1 - \gamma_{N+1}$	βB_{N-1}	$(1+\alpha)A_{N-1} + (1-\beta)B_{N-1}$
(v)	P	1	0	$(1+\alpha)A_{N-1}$	B_{N-1}

this on the first few stages. From (6.7) we have

$$\varphi_1(\gamma_2) = 1, \qquad A_1 = 1, \qquad B_1 = 0. \tag{6.21}$$

Thus $(1 + \alpha)A_1 - 1 > 0$ and $\beta B_1 - 1 < 0$ and we are in cases (ii) or (iii). This gives $A_2 = 1$, $B_2 = \alpha$ for $\gamma_3 < 1$ and $A_2 = (1 + \alpha)$, $B_2 = 0$ for $\gamma_3 > 1$, so

$$\varphi_2(\gamma_3) = \begin{cases} 1 + \alpha\gamma_3 & 0 \leqslant \gamma_3 \leqslant 1 \\ (1 + \alpha) & 1 \leqslant \gamma_3. \end{cases} \tag{6.22}$$

We now have several possibilities for stage 3. In the first place we should check to see if the conditions have changed. Now $(1 + \alpha)A_2 - 1$ is either α or

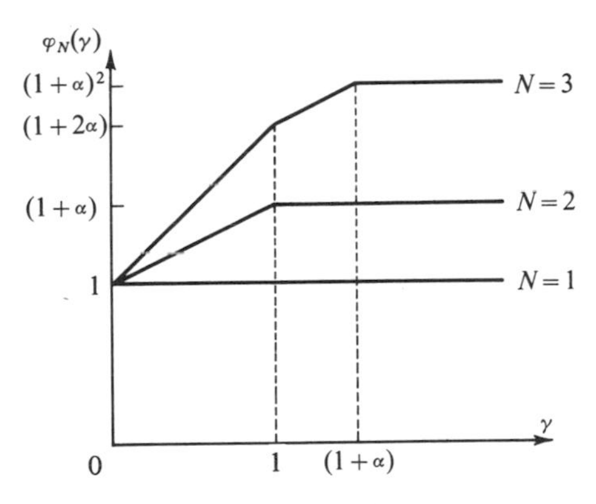

Figure 6.4

$(1 + \alpha)^2 - 1$ and so is still positive. If $\gamma_3 < 1$, $\beta B_2 - 1 = \alpha\beta - 1$ which may be positive and if $\gamma_3 > 1$, $\beta B_2 - 1$ is still negative. Let us suppose for definiteness that $\alpha\beta < 1$, then cases (ii) and (iii) still obtain. We have the possibilities listed in Table 6.4. The functions φ_1, φ_2, and φ_3 are shown in Figure 6.4, with the appropriate policies.

Table 6.4

	η_4	ζ_4	γ_3	A_3	B_3	$(1 + \alpha)A_3 - 1$	$\beta B_3 - 1$
$\gamma_4 \leqslant 1$	γ_4	0	$(1 + \alpha)^{-1}$	1	2α	α	$2\alpha\beta - 1$
$1 \leqslant \gamma_4 \leqslant 1 + \alpha$	1	0	$\gamma_4/(1 + \alpha) \leqslant 1$	$1 + \alpha$	α	$(1 + \alpha)^2 - 1$	$\alpha\beta - 1$
$1 + \alpha \leqslant \gamma_4$	1	0	$\gamma_4/(1 + \alpha) \geqslant 1$	$(1 + \alpha)^2$	0	$(1 + \alpha)^3 - 1$	-1

The pattern has been established and will only change when the condition $\beta B_N < 1$ is changed. This will first happen for $\gamma_{N+1} \leqslant 1$, and will be when N is first greater than $1/\alpha\beta$.

To see what then happens let us take a definite case with $\alpha = 0.5$, $\beta = 1.5$ so that $2\alpha\beta > 1 > \alpha\beta$. Now equation (6.16) reads

$$\gamma_4 = (\gamma_5 + \tfrac{3}{2}\zeta_5)/\tfrac{3}{2}\eta_5$$

and the three regions of importance for γ_4, namely, $\gamma_4 \leqslant 1$, $1 \leqslant \gamma_4 \leqslant 1 + \alpha$, $1 + \alpha \leqslant \gamma_4$, correspond to three regions of the η_5, ζ_5 plane. Thus:

Region	Bounded by	Gives
	$\eta = 0$	
L		$\frac{3}{2} \leqslant \gamma_4$
	$\zeta = \frac{3}{2}\eta - \frac{2}{3}\gamma_5$	
M		$1 \leqslant \gamma_4 \leqslant \frac{3}{2}$
	$\zeta = \eta - \frac{2}{3}\gamma_5$	
N		$\gamma_4 \leqslant 1$
	$\zeta = 0$	

Taking the values of A_3 and B_3 from Table 6.4, equation 6.20 for the choice of (η_5, ζ_5) may be written in each region

$$\begin{aligned}
L:&\quad A_4 + B_4\gamma_5 = \text{Max}\,[\quad 1 \quad + \tfrac{19}{8}\eta_5 - \zeta_5] \\
M:&\quad A_4 + B_4\gamma_5 = \text{Max}\,[(1 + \tfrac{1}{2}\gamma_5) + \tfrac{5}{4}\eta_5 - \tfrac{1}{4}\zeta_5] \\
N:&\quad A_4 + B_4\gamma_5 = \text{Max}\,[(1 + \gamma_5) \;+ \tfrac{1}{2}\eta_5 + \tfrac{1}{2}\zeta_5].
\end{aligned}$$

The level lines of the expression to be maximized run as shown in Figure 6.5 and evidently we have the maximum for region L at the vertex l, that for

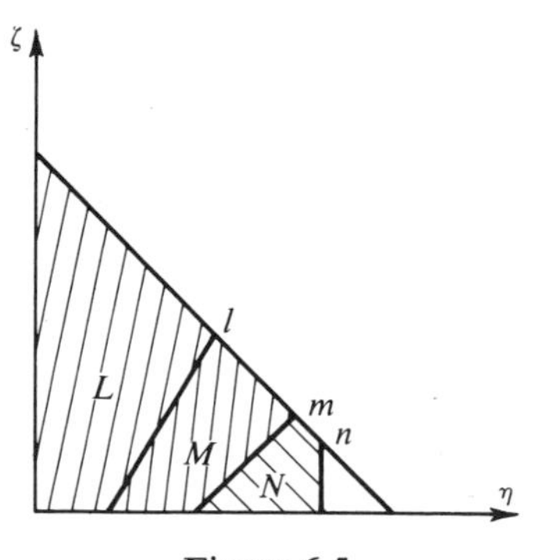

Figure 6.5

region M at m, and for N, through the accident of $\alpha = 2\alpha\beta - 1$, the whole line mn gives the maximum. We have thus only to compare these vertices. Again to take a definite example, if $\gamma_5 = \frac{9}{10}$ we have values at l, m and on mn of 2.16, 2.4, and 2.4, respectively, and thus any part of the segment mn would give an optimal policy. For definiteness the point n may be taken, giving $\eta_5 = \gamma_5$ and $\zeta_5 = 1 - \gamma_5$. Figure 6.6 shows the expression to be maximized. We see that with this decision there is no B left to allocate to the production of A and the policy has entered a phase in which the entire effort is devoted to adapting the situation for later exploitation.

By now it is fairly clear that, though the problem is piecewise linear, the geometrical way in which we have been proceeding is becoming too complicated and it will be necessary to work numerically. The reduction of dimensionality from the two variables x and c to the single ratio γ has already given

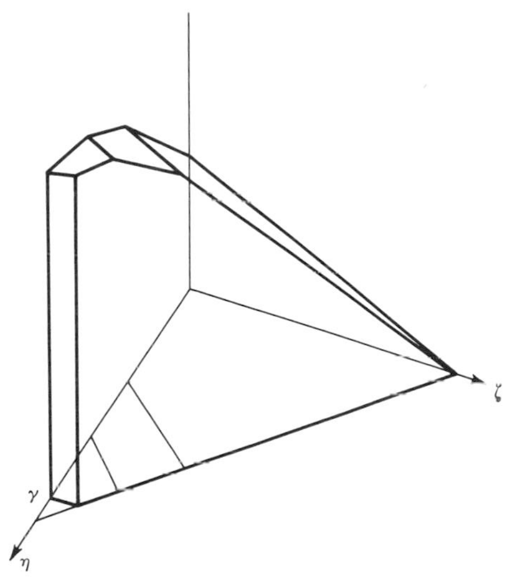

Figure 6.6

us an advantage from the computational point of view, and our geometrical analysis has revealed the piecewise linearity and need to search only a finite number of vertices. But it has also revealed some difficulties. The first of these, which will be overcome in the next section, lies in the fact that a trial policy with a small value of γ_{n+1} may call for a very large value of γ_n in the evaluation of $\varphi_{n+1}(\gamma_n)$. In the geometrical picture of the early cases φ_n was constant for sufficiently large γ and this was no trouble, but a strictly numerical approach would not necessarily reveal this.

The second point that the geometrical approach has revealed is that the functions to be maximized are not given by one formula over the whole policy region and so are given by a number of planes rather than by a single one. This *piecewise* linear character means that the vertices of each subregion (such as L, M, N in Figure 6.5) and not just the vertices of the whole region (as $ORSQ$ in Figure 6.3) must be examined. Rather than finding out just what these subregional vertices are, it is probably better to institute a search along the whole boundary of the admissible policy region. The linearity of the function to be maximized will be detected and can be exploited. The importance of this, which has sometimes been overlooked, would have been evident in the previous example if β had been chosen slightly greater than $\frac{3}{2}$ with α

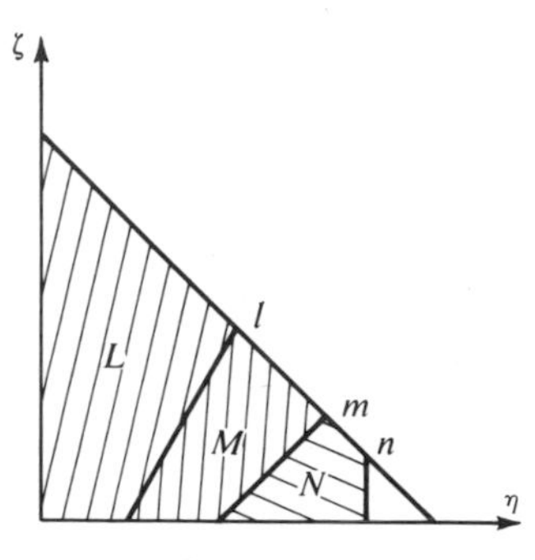

Figure 6.7

still $\frac{1}{2}$. For then with $2\alpha\beta - 1$ greater than α the level lines in the regions M and N would have been as in Figure 6.7 and the point n would give the optimal policy.

6.3. The menace of the expanding grid

The difficulty that arises when a modest value of γ_{n+1} generates a large value of γ_n was early noticed by Bellman, who coined for it the colorful title above. The difficulty lies in the fact that $\varphi_{n+1}(\gamma_n)$ must be calculated and stored for use in calculating $\varphi_n(\gamma_{n+1})$, and storage and interpolation are difficult if γ_n covers a vast range. Bellman's solution is as simple as it is effective, we consider not only γ but also its reciprocal $\delta = 1/\gamma = x/c$. Then when $\gamma > 1$, δ is less than 1 and we can take it as the variable. Since $0 \leqslant \delta \leqslant 1$ there is no more problem in storage and interpolation than there is for γ when $0 \leqslant \gamma \leqslant 1$.

To see this in action we define new functions as follows:

$$\delta_{N+1} = x_{N+1}/c_{N+1} \tag{6.23}$$

$$f_N(x_{N+1}, c_{N+1}) = c_{N+1}\psi_N(\delta_{N+1}) \tag{6.24}$$

whenever $\delta_{N+1} \leqslant 1$. When $\delta_{N+1} \geqslant 1$, that is, $\gamma_{N+1} \leqslant 1$, we retain the definitions (6.11) and (6.12). Now the equation

$$\gamma_n = \frac{\gamma_{n+1} + \beta\zeta_{n+1}}{(1 + \alpha)\eta_{n+1}}$$

can be written in four ways,

$$\gamma_n = \frac{\gamma_{n+1} + \beta\zeta_{n+1}}{(1 + \alpha)\eta_{n+1}} = \frac{1 + \beta\delta_{n+1}\zeta_{n+1}}{(1 + \alpha)\eta_{n+1}\delta_{n+1}}, \tag{6.25}$$

$$\delta_n = \frac{(1 + \alpha)\eta_{n+1}}{\gamma_{n+1} + \beta\zeta_{n+1}} = \frac{(1 + \alpha)\eta_{n+1}\delta_{n+1}}{1 + \beta\delta_{n+1}\zeta_{n+1}}, \tag{6.26}$$

that form being chosen which keeps the γ and/or δ involved less than 1. Similarly we take the basic functional equation (6.6) and divide through by x_{N+1} or c_{N+1}. Dividing through by x_{N+1} gives

$$\varphi_N(\gamma_{N+1}) = \text{Max}\,[1 - \eta_{N+1} - \delta_{N+1} + f_{N-1}(x_N, c_N)/x_{N+1}].$$

If the $f_{N-1}(x_N, c_N)$ is expressed as $x_N\varphi_{N-1}(\gamma_N)$ we have the equation (6.18) of the last section, but this is now inappropriate if γ_N should be greater than one. However if we write $f_{N-1}(x_N, c_N)/x_{N+1}$ as $(c_N/x_{N+1})\psi_{N-1}(\delta_N)$ we have

$$\begin{aligned}\varphi_N(\gamma_{N+1}) &= \text{Max}\,[1 - \eta_{N+1} - \zeta_{N+1} + (1 + \alpha)\eta_{N+1}\psi_{N+1}(\delta_N)/\delta_N] \\ &= \text{Max}\,[1 - \eta_{N+1} - \delta_{N+1} + (1 + \beta\delta_{N+1}\zeta_{N+1})\psi_{N-1}(\delta_N)/\delta_{N+1}].\end{aligned} \tag{6.27}$$

Proceeding in this way we have a tableau of four equations (Table 6.5) to be used in the situations indicated. It is a simple matter to program the computer to choose the correct equation to use and so compute the functions $\varphi_n(\gamma)$ and $\psi_n(\delta)$. The results of the determination of optimal policy can be put into a

Table 6.5

$\gamma_{N+1} < 1$	$\gamma_N < 1$	$\varphi_N(\gamma_{N+1})$ $= \text{Max}\,[1 - \eta_{N+1} - \zeta_{N+1} + (1 + \alpha)\eta_{N+1}\varphi_{N-1}(\gamma_N)]$
$\gamma_{N+1} < 1$	$\delta_N < 1$	$\varphi_N(\gamma_{N+1})$ $= \text{Max}\,[1 - \eta_{N+1} - \zeta_{N+1} + (1 + \beta\delta_{N+1}\zeta_{N+1})\psi_{N-1}(\delta_N)/\delta_{N+1}]$
$\delta_{N+1} < 1$	$\gamma_N < 1$	$\psi_N(\delta_{N+1})$ $= \text{Max}\,[(1 - \eta_{N+1} - \zeta_{N+1})\delta_{N+1} + (1 + \alpha)\eta_{N+1}\delta_{N+1}\varphi_{N-1}(\gamma_N)]$
$\delta_{N+1} < 1$	$\delta_N < 1$	$\psi_N(\delta_{N+1})$ $= \text{Max}\,[(1 - \eta_{N+1} - \zeta_{N+1})\delta_{N+1} + (1 + \beta\delta_{N+1}\zeta_{N+1})\psi_{N-1}(\delta_N)]$

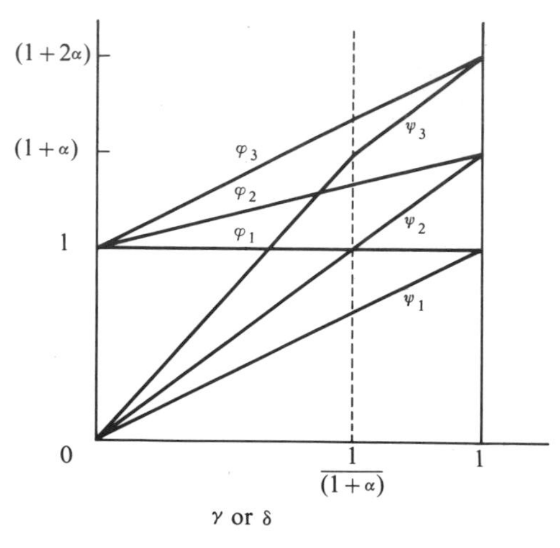

Figure 6.8

graph with a single range of the variable γ or δ, using the relations $\psi(\delta) = \delta\varphi(1/\delta)$ and $\varphi(\gamma) = \gamma\psi(1/\gamma)$. This transformation retains piecewise linearity. For example, Figure 6.4 becomes Figure 6.8.

6.4. The control of economic trends

An elementary model of the dynamics of national income can be constructed as follows. The total national income in year t is denoted by Y_t and is the sum of the consumer expenditure C_t, the induced private investment I_t, and the government expenditure G_t.

$$Y_t = C_t + I_t + G_t. \tag{6.28}$$

The consumer expenditure depends on the national income of the previous year $(t - 1)$ in the fashion

$$C_t = \alpha Y_{t-1}, \tag{6.29}$$

where α is called the marginal propensity to consume. The investment induced in year t depends on the increase in consumer expenditure of that year over the preceding year,

$$I_t = \beta(C_t - C_{t-1}) = \alpha\beta(Y_{t-1} - Y_{t-2}). \tag{6.30}$$

Thus

$$Y_t = \alpha Y_{t-1} + \alpha\beta(Y_{t-1} - Y_{t-2}) + G_t. \tag{6.31}$$

This is a difference equation of the second order in Y_t and can be solved as follows. Consider first the homogeneous equation with $G_t = 0$ and write it

$$Y_t - \alpha(1 + \beta)Y_{t-1} + \alpha\beta Y_{t-2} = 0. \tag{6.32}$$

Suppose there is a solution of the form

$$Y_t = m^t,$$

then substitution in (6.32) shows that m must satisfy

$$m^2 - \alpha(1 + \beta)m + \alpha\beta = 0. \tag{6.33}$$

This gives two values m_1 and m_2 and we see by substitution that, for any constants A_1 and A_2,

$$Y_t = A_1 m_1^t + A_2 m_2^t \tag{6.34}$$

would also be a solution. If the government expenditure were constant (say $G_t = 1$, for we can always take this as the monetary unit) then a particular solution of the inhomogeneous equation with $G_t = 1$ is $Y_t = 1/(1 - \alpha)$. Thus a full solution for constant government expenditure is

$$Y_t = A_1 m_1^t + A_2 m_2^t + 1/(1 - \alpha), \tag{6.35}$$

where A_1 and A_2 would be chosen to fit the national income of the first two years. Now if $|m_1|$ and $|m_2|$ are both less than one m_1^t and m_2^t will tend to zero as t and the national income will approach $1/(1 - \alpha)$ times the government expenditure. If however $|m_1|$ or $|m_2|$ or both should be greater than one the national income will soar or nose-dive or oscillate violently. If m_1 and m_2 are complex numbers with unit modulus the national income will oscillate steadily about its mean value.

A number of optimal problems now spring to mind. How should G_t be chosen to control the fluctuations of the economy in a potentially instable situation? How should it be chosen to give a maximum, or prescribed, value or rate of growth to the national income at some future time? Now doubtless the constants α and β are affected by G_t, since this must be subscribed by taxes which in turn affect the propensities to consume and invest. Since, however, we are not so much concerned with the validity of the economic model let us assume that α and β are constants and remark only that the more complicated problem with $\alpha = \alpha(G)$, $\beta = \beta(G)$ can be solved quite as readily by dynamic programming. Also to take a different form of objective function we will consider the problem of stabilization and try to maximize the minimum national income that occurs in the next N years with no more than a certain total government expenditure.

To cast the problem in the familiar form we regard the target date (the next election or *Dies Irae*) as year 1 and the first year of the N-year period as year N. Then with Y_n denoting the national income in year n and G_n the government expenditure, equation (6.31) may be written

$$Y_n = \alpha Y_{n+1} + \alpha\beta(Y_{n+1} - Y_{n+2}) + G_n. \tag{6.36}$$

The state of the system must be specified by the national income for two adjacent years or equivalently by the income and its increase or decrease from the previous year. Let us set

$$Z_n = Y_n - Y_{n+1}; \tag{6.37}$$

then

$$Y_n = \alpha Y_{n+1} + \alpha\beta Z_{n+1} + G_n \tag{6.38}$$

and

$$Z_n = (\alpha - 1) Y_{n+1} + \alpha\beta Z_{n+1} + G_n. \tag{6.39}$$

Since a fixed total expenditure $\Sigma_1^N G_n$ is imposed we should also take as a state variable the amount available for future spending,

$$H_n = \sum_1^{n-1} G_r = G - \sum_n^N G_r, \tag{6.40}$$

where G is the given total. The state variable H_n is transformed according to the equation

$$H_n = H_{n+1} - G_n. \tag{6.41}$$

We can now write down the problem in standard form.

(i) State: Y_n, Z_n, H_n.
(ii) Decision: G_n.
(iii) Transformation: $Y_n = \alpha Y_{n+1} + \alpha\beta Z_{n+1} + G_n$
$Z_n = (\alpha - 1) Y_{n+1} + \alpha\beta Z_{n+1} + G_n$
$H_n = H_{n+1} - G_n$.
(iv) Constraints: $0 \leqslant G_n \leqslant H_{n+1} \leqslant G$.
(v) Objective function: Maximize $[\text{Min}\,\{Y_1, \cdots, Y_N\}]$.
(vi) Parameters: α, β.

Here $\text{Min}\,\{Y_1, \cdots, Y_n\}$ stands for the least of the values of Y_n, $n = 1, 2, \cdots, N$, and we want the least of these values to be as great as possible. Let

$$f_N(Y_{N+1}, Z_{N+1}, H_{N+1}) = \text{Max}\,[\text{Min}\,\{Y_1, \cdots, Y_N\}], \tag{6.42}$$

where the maximization is by suitable choice of $G_1, \cdots, G_N$. Then applying the principle of optimality G_N should be chosen so as to maximize the lesser of the two quantities Y_N and $\text{Min}\,\{Y_1, \cdots, Y_{N-1}\}$. This leads to the equation

$$f_N(Y_{N+1}, Z_{N+1}, H_{N+1}) = \text{Max}\,[\text{Min}\,\{Y_N, f_{N-1}(Y_N, Z_N, H_N)\}], \tag{6.43}$$

where the maximization is by choice of G_N and the quantities on the right can be evaluated by equations (6.38), (6.39), and (6.41).

To see how this works out let us take a simple example and solve it without attempting any dimensionality reduction. With $\alpha = 0.5$, $\beta = 1$, $Y_4 = 1$, $Z_4 = 0.5$ we have a potentially dangerous situation, for without any government spending the national income would fall catastrophically: $Y_3 = 0.75$, $Y_2 = 0.25$, $Y_1 = -0.125$. With a total government spending of $H_4 = 1$ let us

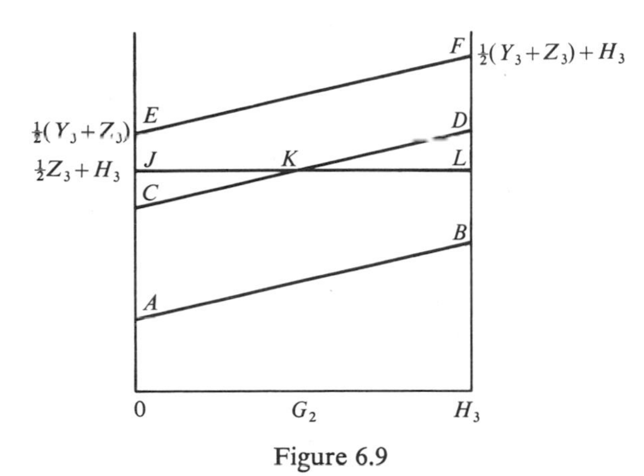

Figure 6.9

see how it could be allocated over the three years to maximize the minimum national income and avert disaster.

For a single year equation (6.43) is trivial, for

$$f_1(Y_2, Z_2, H_2) = \text{Max } Y_1 = \text{Max } [\tfrac{1}{2}(Y_2 + Z_2) + G_2]$$

$$= \tfrac{1}{2}(Y_2 + Z_2) + H_2 \qquad (6.44)$$

and the policy is to spend all that is left,

$$G_1 = H_2. \qquad (6.45)$$

For two years we have

$$f_2(Y_3, Z_3, H_3) = \underset{G_2}{\text{Max}} [\text{Min } \{Y_2, f_1(Y_2, Z_2, H_2)\}]$$

$$= \text{Max } [\text{Min } \{\tfrac{1}{2}(Y_3 + Z_3) + G_2, \tfrac{1}{2}(Y_2 + Z_2) + H_2\}. \qquad (6.46)$$

But by the equations of transformation

$$\tfrac{1}{2}(Y_2 + Z_2) + H_2 = \tfrac{1}{2}Z_3 + H_3,$$

and this is independent of G_2. By drawing the graphs of the two terms that are compared in equation (6.46) we see that there are three cases. In Figure 6.9 the two expressions to be compared are plotted against G_3. The second

$\frac{1}{2}Z_3 + H_3$ is of course constant, and the first $\frac{1}{2}(Y_3 + Z_3) + G_2$ can either lie wholly below, cross it, or lie wholly above. In the first case (the line AB) the upper end $\frac{1}{2}(Y_3 + Z_3) + H_3$ is less than $\frac{1}{2}Z_3 + H_3$, that is, $Y_3 < 0$, the first term $\frac{1}{2}(Y_3 + Z_3) + G_2$ is always less than the second and so G_2 should be chosen to make it as large as possible. Thus $G_2 = H_3$ and $f_2 = \frac{1}{2}(Y_3 + Z_3) + H_3$. In the second case ($CD$) the lower end of the line, $\frac{1}{2}(Y_3 + Z_3)$, is less than $\frac{1}{2}Z_3 + H_3$ but the upper end, $\frac{1}{2}(Y_3 + Z_3) + H_3$ is greater than it; that is, $0 \leqslant Y_3 \leqslant 2H_3$. Now to the left of the intersection point K, $\frac{1}{2}(Y_3 + Z_3) + G_2$

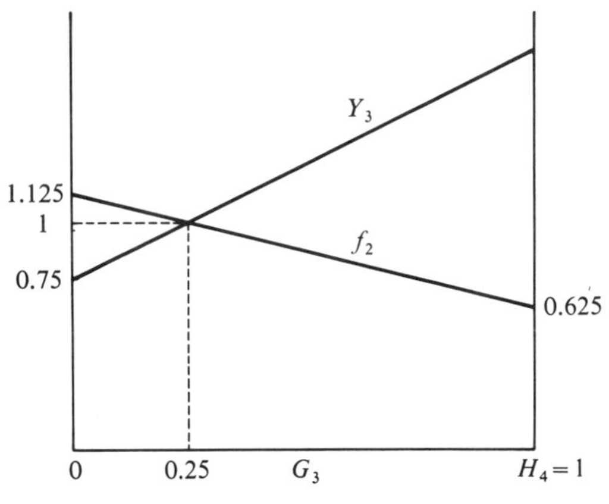

Figure 6.10

is the lesser of the two terms whereas to the right it is $\frac{1}{2}Z_3 + H_3$ that is smaller. Hence if G_2 is chosen to be the value at the point K, the lesser of the two will be as large as possible. This gives $G_2 = H_3 - \frac{1}{2}Y_3$ and $f_2 = \frac{1}{2}Z_3 + H_3$. Again if the line $\frac{1}{2}(Y_3 + Z_3) + G_2$ is disposed as EF entirely above JKL then $f_2 = \frac{1}{2}Z_3 + H_3$ and $G_2 = 0$. Thus we have

$$Y_3 \leqslant 0, \qquad f_2(Y_3, Z_3, H_3) = \tfrac{1}{2}Y_3 + \tfrac{1}{2}Z_3 + H_3, \qquad G_2 = H_3,$$
$$0 \leqslant Y_3 \leqslant 2H_3, \qquad f_2(Y_3, Z_3, H_3) = \tfrac{1}{2}Z_3 + H_3, \qquad G_2 = H_3 - \tfrac{1}{2}Y_3,$$
$$2H_3 \leqslant Y_3, \qquad f_2(Y_3, Z_3, H_3) = \tfrac{1}{2}Z_3 + H_3, \qquad G_2 = 0.$$

Now we can consider the three year plan with $Y_4 = 1$, $Z_4 = 0.5$, and $H_4 = 1$. The values of Y_3, Z_3, and H_3 are given by

$$Y_3 = 0.75 + G_3, \qquad Z_3 = 0.25 + G_3, \qquad H_3 = 1 - G_3.$$

Since G_3 is positive we can never have $Y_3 \leqslant 0$ but $Y_3 \leqslant 2H_3$ if $G_3 \leqslant \frac{5}{12}$. The form of f_2 does not change at this point, however (it is only the policy G_2), and so $f_2 = \frac{1}{2}Z_3 + H_3 = 1.125 - \frac{1}{2}G_3$. Thus the two terms Y_3 and f_2 are as shown in Figure 6.10. The lines intersect at $G_3 = 0.25$ and this choice of G_3 makes the lesser of f_2 and Y_3 as large as possible. With $G_3 = 0.25$, $Y_3 = 1$,

$Z_3 = 0.5$, $H_3 = 0.75$, and $f_3(1, 0.5, 1) = 1$. Since $G_3 < \frac{5}{12} Y_3 < 2H_3$ and the best policy for year 2 is $G_2 = H_3 - \frac{1}{2}Y_3 = 0.25$. Then $Y_2 = 1$, $Z_2 = 0$, $H_2 = 0.5$ and in the final year $G_1 = H_2 = 0.5$ and $Y_1 = 1$. Thus the national income has been maintained at the level 1 by correct distribution of government spending. If this spending had been equally divided between the three years $G_1 = G_2 = G_3 = 0.333$ the national income would have been $Y_3 = 1.416$, $Y_2 = 0.916$, and $Y_3 = 0.541$. It appears therefore that a valuable stabilizing effect can be obtained by correct programming.

6.5. Another trick in dimensionality reduction

We made no attempt in the previous section to reduce the number of arguments of the function f_N, as could have been done by exploiting the linearity as before. Here we wish to show a more subtle exploitation of the linearity of the basic difference equation in a problem for which the objective function is not linear. Let us consider the same model of the dynamics of national income and suppose that the government spending is directed at maximizing the value of Y_1 (year 1 is the next election). However an increase in the national income will not be favorably regarded if it is bought at the price of the taxpayers' blood and the propaganda value of Y_1 must therefore be reduced by $\lambda \Sigma_1^N G_n^2$. The psychology embodied in G_n^2 is that there is a certain level of expenditure $G_n = 1$ which is expected or tolerated as the inevitable. Values of G_n greater than this weigh on the mind more than proportionately, G_n^2 being greater than G_n, but those less than unity are so gratifying as to weigh less than proportionately ($G_n^2 < G_n$). The objective function is thus $Y_1 - \lambda \Sigma_1^N G_n^2$. The reader with a serious cast of mind is reminded that we are not concerned with the validity of the model, but with the way such a model can be optimized.

The problem may now be set up in standard form:

(i) State: Y_n, Z_n.

(ii) Decision: G_n.

(iii) Transformation: $Y_n = \alpha Y_{n+1} + \alpha\beta Z_{n+1} + G_n$,
$$Z_n = (\alpha - 1) Y_{n+1} + \alpha\beta Z_{n+1} + G_n.$$

(iv) Constraints: $G_n \geqslant 0$.

(v) Objective function: Maximize $Y_1 - \lambda \Sigma_1^N G_n^2$.

(vi) Parameters: α, β, λ.

The straightforward application of the principle of optimality would lead us to write

$$f_N(Y_{N+1}, Z_{N+1}) = \text{Max} \left[Y_1 - \lambda \sum_1^N G_n^2 \right] \tag{6.47}$$

and then

$$f_N(Y_{N+1}, Z_{N+1}) = \text{Max}\,[f_{N-1}(Y_N, Z_N) - \lambda G_N^2], \tag{6.48}$$

where in this second maximization we have only to choose G_N. Here we have to carry along functions of the two state variables Y and Z. The reduction to one variable depends on the known form of the solution of the linear difference equation and is entirely analogous to the method for linear differential equations that Bellman discovered. It will effect a reduction to a single variable and though this saving is not so dramatic here the same method applies to an Mth order linear difference equation where it replaces M variables by only one. This is the same case with Mth order differential equations, while with difference-differential equations it replaces a whole function (or a continuously infinite number of variables) by a single one. Such economies are all too rarely possible.

The solution of the equation

$$Y_n - \alpha(1 + \beta)Y_{n+1} + \alpha\beta Y_{n+2} = G_n \tag{6.49}$$

for $N \geqslant n \geqslant 1$ and given Y_{N+1} and $Z_{N+1} = (Y_{N+1} - Y_{N+2})$ is

$$Y_n = \frac{m_1 m_2}{m_1 - m_2}\left[\left\{Z_{N+1} - \left(\frac{m_2 - 1}{m_2}\right)Y_{N+1}\right\}m_1^{N+1-n} - \left\{Z_{N+1} - \frac{m_1 - 1}{m_1}Y_{N+1}\right\}\right.$$
$$\left.\times\, m_2^{N+1-n}\right] + \frac{1}{m_1 - m_2}\sum_{r=n}^{N}[m_1^{r+1-n} - m_2^{r+1-n}]G_r, \tag{6.50}$$

where m_1 and m_2 are the roots of

$$m^2 - \alpha(1 + \beta)m + \alpha\beta = 0. \tag{6.51}$$

This is seen to consist of two parts; the first part is the solution of the homogeneous equation with $G_n \equiv 0$ and represents the value of Y_n that would arise from Y_{N+1} and Z_{N+1} if there were no control in the form of G_n. The second is the sum of the effects at stage n of all the values of G_n at previous stages. In particular we can write for $n = 1$

$$Y_1 = X_{N+1} + \sum_{1}^{N} W_r G_r, \tag{6.52}$$

where

$$W_r = (m_1^r - m_2^r)/(m_1 - m_2), \tag{6.53}$$

$$X_{N+1} = m_1 m_2(Z_{N+1} - Y_{N+1})W_N + Y_{N+1}W_{N+1}. \tag{6.54}$$

Here X_{N+1} is the state Y_1 that would arise from the state Y_{N+1}, Z_{N+1} in the absence of control and we claim that it can be used as the single state variable in this problem. This is to say that all states Y_{N+1}, Z_{N+1} that give the same Y_1 without control are equivalent for this problem.

To establish the method let us first see how X_{N+1} is transformed to X_N. If there were control only for stage N and the G_n, $n = N - 1, \cdots, 2, 1$, were all zero the value of Y_1 would be $X_{N+1} + W_N G_N$ and this can be regarded as the value of Y_1 that could be attained from X_N with no control. Thus

$$X_n = X_{n+1} + W_n G_n. \tag{6.55}$$

Now let

$$\varphi_N(X_{N+1}) = \text{Max}\left[Y_1 - \lambda \sum_1^N G_n^2\right], \tag{6.56}$$

that is, the maximum value of $Y_1 - \lambda\Sigma G_n^2$ that can be attained by the optimal choice of $G_1, \cdots, G_N$ if the value of Y_1 without control would be X_{N+1}. Then an application of the principle of optimality gives

$$\varphi_N(X_{N+1}) = \underset{G_N}{\text{Max}}\,[\varphi_{N-1}(X_N) - \lambda G_N^2], \tag{6.57}$$

since undoubtedly the optimal policy must be used for the remaining stages and λG_N^2 is the cost of the trial value G_N for stage N.

This problem has a particularly simple analytic solution which may be obtained by induction or confirmed by direct substitution. It is

$$\varphi_N(X_{N+1}) = X_{N+1} + \sum_1^N W_n^2/4\lambda \tag{6.58}$$

with the policy

$$G_n = W_n/2\lambda. \tag{6.59}$$

Since φ_N is the maximum of $Y_1 - \lambda\Sigma_1^N G_n^2$ it follows that the maximum value of Y_1 actually attained is $X_{N+1} + \Sigma_1^N W_n^2/2\lambda$. This means that it exceeds the value of Y_1 without control by $\Sigma_1^N W_n^2/2\lambda$.

The complete solution of the Mth order difference equation

$$Y_n + \alpha_1 Y_{n+1} + \alpha_2 Y_{n+2} + \cdots \alpha_M Y_{n+M} = G_n \tag{6.60}$$

requires the specification of M quantities $Y_{N+1}, Y_{N+2}, \cdots, Y_{N+M}$ (or differences formed from them) and its solution has the same form

$$Y_n = \sum_{j=1}^M A_j m_j^{N+1-n} + \sum_n^N W_r G_r, \tag{6.61}$$

where the A_j are chosen to fit the specified values and the m_j are roots of the equation

$$m^M + \alpha_1 m^{M-1} + \cdots + \alpha_M = 0. \tag{6.62}$$

For $n = 1$ the first term again represents the value of Y_1 without control and may be taken to be the state variable X_{N+1}. This effects a reduction in the number of variables from M to 1.

6.6. The control of competitive processes

Let us consider the possibility of optimal advertising in a competitive situation. The soap industry of a certain country is controlled by a triumvirate of three companies known to Madison Avenue as L, B, and W. The makers of Beauty Bath (and other alliterative preparations), B, occupy a favored central position for it appears that when the devotees of Lovely Lave and Wonder Wash indulge in an agonizing reappraisal of their ablutionary adjuncts they always change first to Beauty Bath. The makers of B wish to take advantage of this situation and conduct their advertising campaign with such a cunning combination of coupons, catch phrases, and cajolery as to convert as many consumers as possible to their confection. Their advisers have determined that when the tempo of the campaign is T it will lure a fraction λ of the users of L and win a fraction μ of the users of W in the unit of time. Unfortunately, it will also disenchant some of their own users of whom they will lose a fraction l to L and m to W. The fractions λ, μ, l, and m are functions of T and to simplify the decision for the directors only two campaign plans have been produced with tempos $T_{(1)}$ and $T_{(2)}$ and corresponding fractions λ_1, μ_1, l_1, m_1, and λ_2, μ_2, l_2, m_2. Setting a target date of N units of time in the future, how should the directors unfold their campaign?

As usual we number the time intervals from the end to the beginning and let x_n, y_n, and z_n be the fractions of the population addicted to L, B, and W at the end of period n. We are therefore given x_{N+1}, y_{N+1}, and z_{N+1} and wish to choose the sequence of tempos $T_N, T_{N-1}, \cdots, T_1$ (where T_n is either $T_{(1)}$ or $T_{(2)}$) so as to maximize y_1. From what has been said about the results of the advertising we can write down the transformations. For example, the change in y over the nth interval $(y_n - y_{n+1})$ is due to gains λx_{n+1} and μz_{n+1} from the opposing camps and losses $(l + m)y_{n+1}$, giving $y_n = \lambda x_{n+1} + (1 - l - m)y_{n+1} + \mu z_{n+1}$. Thus,

$$x_n = (1 - \lambda)x_{n+1} + ly_{n+1}, \tag{6.63}$$

$$y_n = \lambda x_{n+1} + (1 - l - m)y_{n+1} + \mu z_{n+1}, \tag{6.64}$$

$$z_n = my_{n+1} + (1 - \mu)z_{n+1}, \tag{6.65}$$

which is consistent with the constancy of

$$x_n + y_n + z_n = 1. \tag{6.66}$$

Since we are assuming a constant total population so that x, y, and z are fractions with constant sum, we really have only two variables since equation (6.66) could be used to express any one of them in terms of the other two. However we shall retain all three as this keeps our expressions homogeneous.

For definiteness let us now list the values of the constants for $T_{(1)}$ and $T_{(2)}$.

Tempo	λ	l	m	μ	$1-l-m$
$T_{(1)}$	0.20	0.20	0.20	0.20	0.60
$T_{(2)}$	0.04	0.01	0.01	0.12	0.98

It is noticeable that $T_{(1)}$ is considerably more provocative than $T_{(2)}$ resulting in large fractional changes. However the more soothing $T_{(2)}$ is advantageous

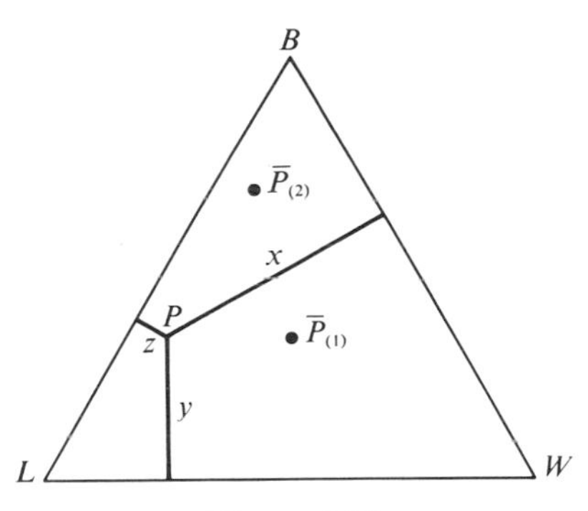

Figure 6.11

to B since its 2% loss is more than compensated by 4% and 12% gains from L and W. In fact we see that equations (6.63), (6.64), and (6.65) have an equilibrium solution

$$\frac{\bar{x}}{l/\lambda} = \bar{y} = \frac{\bar{z}}{m/\mu} = \frac{1}{1 + l/\lambda + m/\mu} \tag{6.67}$$

and when $x_{n+1} = \bar{x}$, etc., so is $x_n = \bar{x}$. The equilibrium solution for $T_{(1)}$ is $\bar{x}_1 = \bar{y}_1 = \bar{z}_1 = \frac{1}{3}$, but this is far less favorable than that for $T_{(2)}$ with $\bar{x}_2 = \frac{3}{16}$, $\bar{y}_2 = \frac{3}{4}$, $\bar{z}_2 = \frac{1}{16}$.

The state of the consumer population at any time can be represented by a point $P(x, y, z)$ on a triangular diagram as in Figure 6.11. In this Figure, x is the perpendicular distance from P to the side BW, y to the side LW, and z to the side LB. By elementary geometry the sum of these is always unity and the vertices are the points (1, 0, 0), (0, 1, 0), and (0, 0, 1). The two equilibrium points $\bar{P}_{(1)}$ and $\bar{P}_{(2)}$ are marked on Figure 6.11 and if only one policy were used (say $T_{(1)}$) the sequence of states (x_n, y_n, z_n), $n = N+1, N, \cdots, 2, 1$, could be represented by a sequence of points $P_{N+1}, P_N, \cdots, P_1$ which would be found to approach $\bar{P}_{(1)}$. In terms of this diagram the objective is to force the point P_1 as far up as possible.

We can now formulate the problem in standard fashion.

(i) State: x_n, y_n, z_n.

(ii) Decision: T_n.

(iii) Transformation: $x_n = (1 - \lambda)x_{n+1} + l y_{n+1}$,

$$y_n = \lambda x_{n+1} + (1 - l - m)y_{n+1} + \mu z_{n+1},$$

$$z_n = m y_{n+1} + (1 - \mu)z_{n+1},$$

where λ, l, m, and μ are functions of T_n.

(iv) Constraints: $x_n + y_n + z_n = 1$, $x_n \geqslant 0$, $y_n \geqslant 0$, $z_n \geqslant 0$, $T_n = T_{(1)}$ or $T_{(2)}$.

(v) Parameters: $\lambda_i = \lambda(T_{(i)})$, etc. are tabulated values.

Let

$$f_N(x_{N+1}, y_{N+1}, z_{N+1}) = \text{Max}\, y_1, \tag{6.68}$$

to be secured by the correct sequence $T_N, \cdots, T_1$. Then by the principle of optimality

$$f_N(x_{N+1}, y_{N+1}, z_{N+1}) = \text{Max}\, [f_{N-1}(x_N, y_N, z_N)], \tag{6.69}$$

where only T_N has to be chosen.

Starting as usual from the single stage we have

$$f_1(x_2, y_2, z_2) = \text{Max}\, [\lambda x_2 + (1 - l - m)y_2 + \mu z_2] \tag{6.70}$$

and the maximization is secured by the correct choice of the set of coefficients λ, l, m, μ. With the constants given above the two alternative values are $(0.2x_2 + 0.6y_2 + 0.2z_2)$ and $(0.04x_2 + 0.98y_2 + 0.12z_2)$. Clearly the second alternative is better when y_2 is large compared with x_2 and z_2 and the two give the same value of y_1 when

$$0.16x_2 - 0.38y_2 + 0.08z_2 = 0.$$

This is the line CD in Figure 6.12 and if the state of the market is represented by a point P above this line $T_{(2)}$ is better than $T_{(1)}$. To obtain the contours y_1 = constant under the optimal policy we recall that $x_2 + y_2 + z_2 = 1$ and write for $T_{(1)}$

$$0.2x_2 + 0.6y_2 + 0.2z_2 = y_1(x_2 + y_2 + z_2),$$

so that a constant y_1 is given by

$$(0.2 - y_1)x_2 + (0.6 - y_1)y_2 + (0.2 - y_1)z_2 = 0.$$

Evidently y_1 is at least 0.2 and rises to 0.32 at the point C. The contours of constant y_1 in the upper region are

$$(0.04 - y_1)x_2 + (0.98 - y_1)y_2 + (0.12 - y_1)z_2 = 0$$

and show that the value of y_1 increases from 0.27 at D to 0.98 at B.

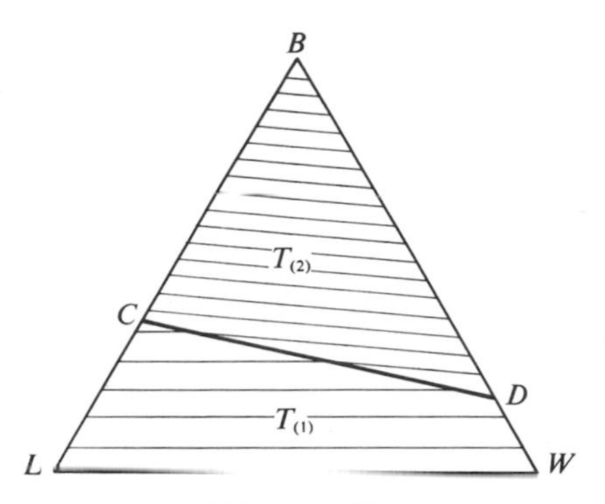

Figure 6.12

In devising the two-stage policy we have to consider into which of these regions the state (x_3, y_3, z_3) is moved by the two possible transformations of stage 2. Since everything is linear we need only consider the transformation of

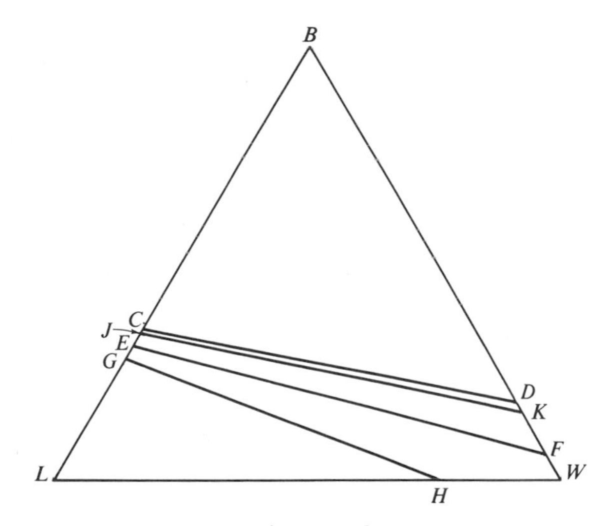

Figure 6.13

the boundary line CD. We find that the line GH of Figure 6.13 is moved by $T_{(1)}$ into CD: its equation is

$$0.054x_3 - 0.180y_3 - 0.012z_3 = 0.$$

Hence anything below this line must transform into a point below the line CD if $T_2 = T_{(1)}$. On the other hand, we have the line EF from CD by the transformation $T_{(2)}$ and its equation is

$$0.138x_3 - 0.380y_3 + 0.025z_3 = 0.$$

Consider a point in the region LGH, both tempo $T_{(1)}$ and tempo $T_{(2)}$ will transform the point (x_3, y_3, z_3) into a point (x_2, y_2, z_2) below the line CD. Hence whatever T_2 may be, T_1 will certainly be $T_{(1)}$, and we therefore want f_1 to be as great as possible. But the contours of constant f_1 are lines of constant y_2 and we have already seen that for this region $T_{(1)}$ gives the largest value of y on transformation. Hence for (x_3, y_3, z_3) in LGH, $T_2 = T_{(1)}$, $T_1 = T_{(1)}$ and the contours are as shown.

For $P_3(x_3, y_3, z_3)$ in the region $GHWFE$ we must proceed more cautiously, for $T_2 = T_{(1)}$ gives a point P_2 above CD but $T_2 = T_{(2)}$ gives a P_2 below it. Thus the choice $T_2 = T_{(1)}$ gives $y_1 = 0.416x_3 + 0.620y_3 + 0.298z_3$, while a choice of $T_2 = T_{(2)}$ gives $y_1 = 0.216x_3 + 0.592y_3 + 0.248z_3$. These two give the same value along the line

$$0.200x_3 + 0.028y_3 + 0.050z_3 = 0.$$

Since this line does not intersect the triangle at all $T_2 = T_{(1)}$ is undoubtedly the better choice in the whole region $GHWFE$ and it will be followed by $T_1 = T_{(2)}$.

For P_3 in EFB both $T_{(1)}$ and $T_{(2)}$ will give a point P_2 in CDB, but $T_2 = T_{(1)}$ gives

$$y_1 = 0.228x_3 + 0.620y_3 + 0.292z_3$$

whereas $T_2 = T_{(2)}$ gives

$$y_1 = 0.078x_3 + 0.962y_3 + 0.223z_3.$$

These give the same value along the line

$$0.150x_3 - 0.342y_3 + 0.069z_3 = 0$$

shown in Figure 6.13 as JK (not greatly differing from CD). It follows that the space has now been divided into three regions:

(i) LGH: $f_2 = 0.180x_3 + 0.440y_3 + 0.180z_3$: $T_2 = T_1 = T_{(1)}$;

(ii) $GHKJ$: $f_2 = 0.228x_3 + 0.620y_3 + 0.292z_3$: $T_2 = T_{(1)}$, $T_1 = T_{(2)}$;

(iii) JKB: $f_2 = 0.078x_3 + 0.962y_3 + 0.223z_3$: $T_2 = T_1 = T_{(2)}$.

Figure 6.14 shows the optimal two stage policy with contours of constant f_2. It is quite evident that the method here represented in the homogeneous coordinate plane allows of a straightforward computer program and will lead to a diagram with $(N + 1)$ regions corresponding to optimal N stage policies of

$$T_n = \begin{Bmatrix} T_{(1)}, & N \geqslant n \geqslant r + 1 \\ T_{(2)}, & r \geqslant n \geqslant 1 \end{Bmatrix}, \quad r = 0, 1, \cdots, N.$$

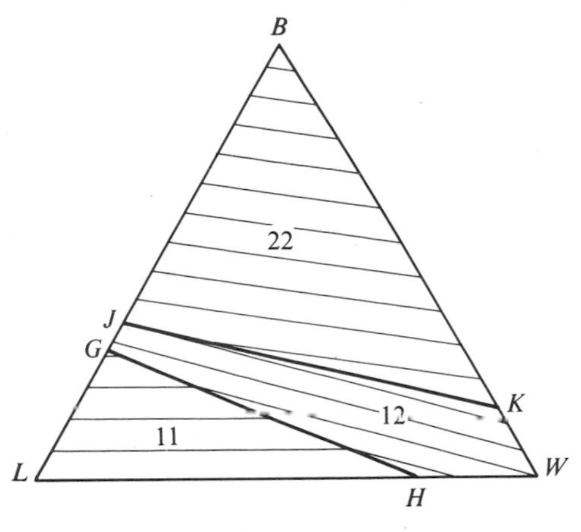

Figure 6.14

The whole problem can be most neatly treated by use of matrices, but we have stayed with simple algebra in the interests of a really elementary treatment.

6.7. Review of the techniques of dimensionality reduction

This is a convenient point to review the various devices that have been introduced to reduce the dimensionality of problems, a matter whose importance cannot be overemphasized. The principal method is the use of the Lagrange multiplier, the subject of Chapter 5. This allows problems with restrictions (for which some measure of the extent to which the restriction has already been met must be included as a state variable) to be treated as unrestricted problems with fewer variables.

The methods of the present chapter have been based on the advantage that can be taken of the linearity of equations. When equations are homogeneous and linear it is possible to work with the ratios of the variables instead of the variables themselves. A difficulty that arises here is that these ratios become very large through the diminishing of the denominator. This can be overcome by using both the ratio and its inverse. A second advantage that can be taken of linear equations is that there exists a closed form of solution of the general linear difference equations. This consists in two parts, the first of which represents the solution of the equation without any control; it depends on the initial values of the state variables and may sometimes be taken as a single variable sufficient to characterize the state.

A further device that has recently been proposed by Bellman is appropriate to a class of problems where the idea of a relative state can be introduced. If a reference state $\tilde{\mathbf{p}}$ can be introduced and the difference $\mathbf{p} - \tilde{\mathbf{p}}$ between the state $\mathbf{p}$ and this reference state contains relatively few variables of significant magnitude, these few may be taken as the relative state variables and the functional equation formulated in terms of them. As yet no concrete examples of this idea have been presented.

Another idea which is being developed and which should prove of the greatest value is that of polynomial approximation. If a function of four or five variables is involved it is a major undertaking to calculate, store, and interpolate even with a comparatively coarse grid of, say, 10 values per variable. However, an approximating polynomial of degree k in the same number of variables has far fewer coefficients. For example with five variables the grid would require 10^5 points but an approximating cubic has only 56 coefficients.

Bellman and Dreyfus [*Applied Dynamic Programming* (Bibliography 1.8), pp. 322–326] give an example of the use of polynomial approximation with one variable. The use of orthogonal polynomials and Gaussian quadrature suggests itself as making the best use of the material to be fitted. For example if the argument x of $f(x)$ is in interval $(-1, 1)$ the Legendre polynomial $P_n(x)$ might be used. For a large class of functions

$$f(x) = \sum_0^\infty a_n P_n(x),$$

where

$$a_n = \int_{-1}^{1} f(x) P_n(x)\, dx.$$

Moreover the a_n so calculated give the best values (in a least squares sense) for the fitting of a truncated series $\Sigma_0^k a_n P_n(x)$. To calculate the coefficients a_n we do not want to go back to a fine grid of points such as we have been trying to evade and so are led to Gaussian quadrature. This replaces the integral by a weighted sum of R values of the integrand at certain points. The weights μ_r and points of evaluation x_r can be determined so that the formula is exact for polynomials of degree up to $(2R - 1)$. Then

$$a_n = \sum_{r=1}^{R} \mu_r P_n(x_r) f(x_r)$$

and for given $k \leqslant 2R - 1$ the weighting factors $\mu_r P_n(x_r)$, $n = 1, \cdots, k$ can be calculated and stored for immediate use. In fact the recurrence relation for the Legendre polynomial may be used to generate the successive $P_n(x_r)$ at the points x_r, which are admittedly odd values. The extension to a higher number of variables is of course nontrivial, but the essential ideas are present here.

Bibliography

6.1. A number of these problems have been treated before. References to these as well as to a large number of other problems of economic interest can be found in the books of Bellman (Bibliography 1.8). In particular Chapters 6 and 7 of *Dynamic Programming* and Chapter 7 of *Applied Dynamic Programming* should be referred to.

6.4. The elementary model of the dynamics of national income was taken from

GOLDBERG, S., *Introduction to Difference Equations*. New York: John Wiley & Sons, Inc., 1961.

He follows

SAMUELSON, P. A., "Interactions between the Multiplier Analysis and the Principle of Acceleration," *Rev. Econ. Statist.*, **21** (1939), 75.

See also

SAMUELSON, P. A., *Foundations of Economic Analysis*. Cambridge: Harvard University Press, 1948.

KARLIN, S., *Mathematical Methods and Theory in Games, Programming, and Economics*. London: Pergamon Press, Inc., and Reading: Addison-Wesley Publishing Co., Inc., 1959.

SCHWARTZ, J. T., *Lectures on the Mathematical Method in Analytical Economics*. New York: Gordon & Breach Science Publishers, Inc., 1961.

ARROW, K. J., KARLIN, S., and SCARF, H., *Studies in the Mathematical Theory of Inventory and Production*. Stanford: Stanford University Press, 1958.

HOWARD, R. A., *Dynamic Programming and Markov Processes*. New York: John Wiley & Sons, Inc., 1960.

6.5. This is an application to difference equations of the method developed in:

BELLMAN, R., and KALABA, R., "Reduction of Dimensionality, Dynamic Programming, and Control Processes," *J. Basic Eng.*, **83** (1961), 82.

6.6. For a matrix problem associated with this section see:

BELLMAN, R., *Introduction to Matrix Analysis*. New York: McGraw-Hill Book Co., Inc., 1960 (p. 155).

6.7. See BELLMAN, R., "On the Reduction of Dimensionality for Classes of Dynamic Programming Processes," *J. Math. Anal. Appl.*, **3** (1961), 358.

BELLMAN, R., and DREYFUS, S. E., "Functional Approximation and Dynamic Programming," *Math. Tables and Aids to Computation*, **13** (1959), 247.

See also Chapter 12 of BELLMAN, *Applied Dynamic Programming* (Bibliography 1.8).

Problems

1. Show that the pattern established in section 6.2 when $N\alpha\beta < 1$ is:

Range of	γ_{N+1}	η_{N+1}	ζ_{N+1}	A_N	B_N
0,	1	γ_{N+1}	0	1	$(N-1)\alpha$
1,	$1+\alpha$	1	0	$1+\alpha$	$(N-2)\alpha$
$1+\alpha$,	$(1+\alpha)^2$	1	0	$(1+\alpha)^2$	$(N-3)\alpha$
$(1+\alpha)^{N-1}$,	∞	1	0	$(1+\alpha)^{N-1}$	0

2. Formulate some of the other optimal control problems mentioned in section 6.4.
3. Propose a model of the national income in which the coefficients α and β are modified by government expenditure through the influence of taxation. Formulate the control problems with this model.
4. Solemnize the example of section 6.6 by showing it is equivalent to the problem of choosing the between two temperatures in a cascade of stirred-tank reactors in which the first-order reversible reactions

$$A \rightleftharpoons B \rightleftharpoons C$$

are taking place.
5. Generalize this model to the case where the temperature can be chosen in the range $T_* \leqslant T \leqslant T^*$ and show that the lines of constant $f_1(x_2, y_2, z_2)$ envelope a curve that can be parametrized with T^0, the optimal temperature.
6. Set up an optimal problem of the type discussed in section 6.6 when the total population changes in a predictable manner.
7. $A^{(1)}$ and $A^{(2)}$ are two fixed matrices and the vector $\mathbf{x}_0$ is transformed to $\mathbf{x}_N$ by $\mathbf{x}_N = A_N A_{N-1} \cdots A_1 \mathbf{x}_0$, where the A_n are either $A^{(1)}$ or $A^{(2)}$. If $\mathbf{c}$ is a fixed vector develop an algorithm for finding the maximum of $\mathbf{c}' \cdot \mathbf{x}$.
8. In a certain model of the business cycle the production $a(t)$ and inventory $b(t)$ on "day" t are governed by the equations

$$a(t) = \gamma a(t-1) - b(t-1) + h$$

$$b(t) = \epsilon a(t-1) + b(t-1) - e,$$

where γ and ϵ are constants and h and e are related to the excess over basic inventory and the self consumption. Set up an objective function in terms of a and b at some predetermined target date and develop an algorithm for optimizing this by control of e and h within certain limits.

9. For fixed e and h these equations have a steady state (Keynes point) at which production and inventory are just balanced. Given the ability to vary e and h in a certain range about the steady state values, how should they be controlled to drive the system to its Keynes point as rapidly as possible?
10. A retailer makes up his inventory of a certain item by an evening order of a certain number from the wholesaler. The cost of r items so ordered is $c(r)$ but if they are ordered during the day to meet an excess demand their price goes up to $p(r)$. The daily demand fluctuates but has a fixed probability distribution, $d(r)$ being the probability that there will be a demand for r items. If the initial stock is s_{N+1} we define $f_N(s_{N+1})$ to be the minimum expected total cost of meeting the demand during the next N days. Show that

$$f_1(s_2) = \min_{s_1 \geqslant s_2} \left[c(s_1 - s_2) + \sum_{s_1}^{\infty} d(r) p(r - s_1) \right]$$

and

$$f_N(s_{N+1}) = \min_{s_N \geqslant s_{N+1}} \left[\begin{array}{l} c(s_N - s_{N+1}) + \sum_{s_N}^{\infty} d(r) p(r - s_N) \\ + f_{N-1}(0) \sum_{s_N}^{\infty} d(r) + \sum_{0}^{s_N} f_N(s_N - r)\, d(r) \end{array} \right].$$

11. If $N \to \infty$ we must introduce a discount ratio a, $0 < a < 1$, to prevent the limit from becoming infinite, and items paid for n days later only cost a^n times their nominal cost. Find the recursive equation for unbounded time.
12. How should the equations be modified if an item ordered on the previous evening takes 36 hours (instead of 12) to arrive? [Many problems of this sort are posed and solved in Bellman, *Dynamic Programming* (Bibliography 1.8), Chapter 5.]

CHAPTER 7

Some problems of communication and information theory

In this chapter we shall consider one or two problems related to communication. They serve to show the versatility of dynamic programming rather than to give an ordered treatment of communication theory.

7.1. The gambler and the faulty telephone cable

A gambler receives advance information on the outcome of independent sporting events and on the basis of this he places his bets. The only jarring feature in this happy state of affairs is the fact that the communication channel is faulty and there is only a probability p (<1) that he will hear the right result. So corrupting is the noise in the channel that there is a probability $q = 1 - p$ that what he hears is the wrong result. [Alternatively one may say that he hears the right result with probability p' and otherwise the noise obliterates the message and he has to make up his mind. If he has no *a priori* information the probability of correctly making up his mind will be $\frac{1}{2}(1 - p')$ so that the total probability of being right is $p = \frac{1}{2}(1 + p')$ and of being wrong is $q = \frac{1}{2}(1 - p')$.] If the gambler starts with a capital x, how much should he bet to maximize his capital after N events?

Clearly $p > \frac{1}{2}$ is the case of interest for otherwise the gambler would place his bets on the team that he hears has lost. If there is just one event and he bets an amount y, then his expected return is

$$p(x + y) + q(x - y) = x + (p - q)y.$$

Since $p > q$ this is maximized by betting all he has with a maximum expected return of

$$f_1(x) = 2px,$$

and a probability $(1 - p)$ of losing all. On two events if he bets y at the first one there is a probability p that he will increase his capital to $(x + y)$ and so be able to increase it further to $2p(x + y)$ on the final event. But there is also a probability q of its reduction to $(x - y)$ with a final expectation of only $2p(x - y)$. Thus y must be chosen to maximize

$$p2p(x + y) + q2p(x - y) = 2p\{x + (p - q)y\}$$

and again the decision is to wager all. Thus

$$f_2(x) = (2p)^2x$$

but there is a probability $(1 - p^2)$ of his being ruined completely. In general, for N events

$$f_N(x) = (2p)^N(x)$$

with a probability $(1 - p^N)$ of ruination; since $p < 1$, p^N rapidly becomes small and the probability of ruination rapidly becomes a certainty.

As a measure of the value of a communication channel such a gambler fears his fate too little or has deserts that are too great. A more conservative "investor" who, though he may fall on evil days, is at least certain to retain some of his capital is a better measure. A gambler who is content to maximize the logarithm of his capital will do this. After one bet of amount y the expected value of the logarithm of his capital is

$$p \log (x + y) + q \log (x - y) \tag{7.1}$$

and the maximum of this is when

$$\frac{p}{x + y} = \frac{q}{x - y}$$

or

$$y = (p - q)x. \tag{7.2}$$

Then $x + y = 2px$ and $x - y = 2qx$ giving an expected return

$$f_1(x) = \log x + (p \log p + q \log q + \log 2). \tag{7.3}$$

It is to be noted that the logarithm of the capital is increased by a constant that depends only on p, that is, the capital itself is increased by a constant factor, which approaches 2 as p approaches 1.

To formulate the N stage policy we may define $f_N(x)$ to be the maximum expected value of the logarithm of the capital after N transactions starting with capital x. As usual it will be convenient to number the bets from the end to the beginning so that for an N-stage process, the first is stage N and the last stage 1. Then by the principle of optimality if an amount y is wagered at the first stage it must be followed by the optimal $(N - 1)$ stage policy. If the first outcome is successful the expected final return will be $f_{N-1}(x + y)$, but if unsuccessful, $f_{N-1}(x - y)$. Therefore we have

$$f_N(x) = \operatorname*{Max}_y \{pf_{N-1}(x + y) + qf_{N-1}(x - y)\}. \tag{7.4}$$

From the form of f_1 we see that $f_2(x)$ is

$$f_2(x) = \operatorname*{Max}_y \{p \log (x + y) + q \log (x - y) + p \log p + q \log q + \log 2\}$$

and the part of this expression that is variable is exactly the same as equation (7.1) that had to be maximized to give $f_1(x)$. It follows that the maximum is again given by $y = (p - q)x$ and

$$f_2(x) = \log x + 2\{p \log p + q \log q + \log 2\}.$$

This suggests that in general

$$f_N(x) = \log x + N\{p \log p + q \log q + \log 2\} \tag{7.5}$$

and this may easily be proved by substituting in equation (7.4). It is left as an exercise to the reader.

The quantity $\{p \log p + q \log q + \log 2\}$ or $\log 2p^pq^q$ is in some sense a measure of the usefulness of the communication channel for $2p^pq^q$ is the greatest possible factor by which the gambler can multiply his capital at each stage. In information theory $-(p \log p + q \log q)$ is known as the entropy of the message, so that our expression is just a particular normalization of the negative entropy or information conveyed.

7.2. The erratic channel

We have supposed that p was a fixed probability and did not change from one event to the next. In contrast to this, an erratic channel would be one for which the p varied from event to event. Consider the problem of maximizing the logarithm of the capital in N stages when p takes on the values p_N, $p_{N-1}, \cdots, p_1$; again p_1 is the probability of correct transmission at the last event of the sequence of N. Then

$$f_1(x) = \operatorname*{Max}_y \{p_1 \log (x + y) + q_1 \log (x - y)\}$$

and as before $y = (p_1 - q_1)x$ and

$$f_1(x) = \log x + p_1 \log p_1 + q_1 \log q_1 + \log 2.$$

For purposes of calculating $f_2(x)$ we must remember that for the first of the two events the probability of correct transmission is p_2 and is this is successful the maximum capital will be $f_1(x + y)$. Similarly if it is unsuccessful, and the probability for this is q_2, the capital may be expected to be $f_1(x - y)$. Thus

$$f_2(x) = \operatorname*{Max}_y \{p_2 f_1(x + y) + q_2 f_1(x - y)\}$$
$$= \operatorname{Max} \{p_2 \log (x + y) + q_2 \log (x - y) + I_1\},$$

where

$$I_n = p_n \log p_n + q_n \log q_n + \log 2.$$

Again all the variation is in the first two terms and their maximum as we have seen several times is $(\log x + I_2)$. Thus

$$f_2(x) = \log x + I_2 + I_1.$$

In general the principle of optimality gives

$$f_N(x) = \operatorname*{Max}_y \{p_N f_{N-1}(x + y) + q_N f_{N-1}(x - y)\}.$$

The solution of this may be obtained quite simply by induction and is

$$f_N(x) = \log x + \sum_1^N I_n.$$

This is only the first of several generalizations that might be made, but which we shall not pursue here. They are discussed in Chapter 17 of Bellman's *Adaptive control processes* (Bibliography 1.8).

7.3. Communications through networks

We turn instead to a class of problems in the optimal routing through a network. Here we consider a network of links between N points, or nodes, such

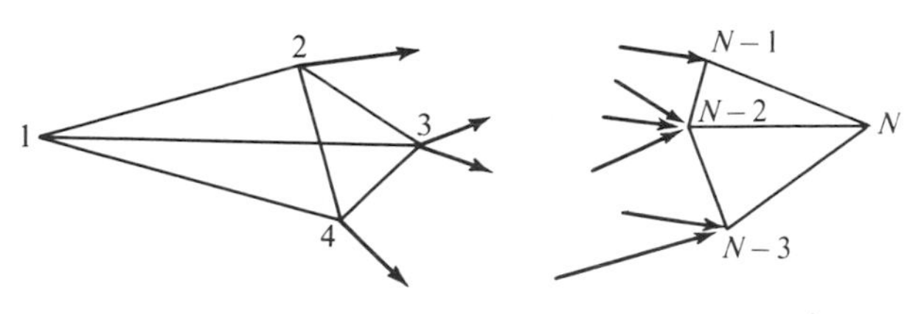

Figure 7.1

as in Figure 7.1. It will be seen that the simple straight chain character of the normal dynamic programming problem is conspicuously absent and, accordingly, we shall not be surprised if the recursive solution of the equations breaks down. The connection of the network is specified by giving the time t_{ij}

taken to get a message from node i to node j. If there is no connection between nodes i and j we can set $t_{ij} = \infty$. The problem is to choose a sequence of nodes between node 1 and node N that will involve the minimum time. The same problem could be formulated in terms of distance rather than time.

Let T_i be the minimum total time from node i to node N given by an appropriate sequence of nodes $i, j, k, \cdots, N$. Now whatever choice is made for j, the node immediately after i, it must certainly be followed by the optimal route from j to N. Hence

$$T_i = \min_{j \neq i} \{t_{ij} + T_j\} \tag{7.6}$$

and by definition of the problem

$$T_N = 0. \tag{7.7}$$

Here, however, we have not a set of equations that can be solved recursively for all the T_j on the right-hand side of the equation need to be known to evaluate the T_i on the left.

Instead we proceed by successive approximations in a way which does in fact reduce it to a sequential process. Let

$$f_k(i) = \text{Minimum time from } i \text{ to } N, \text{ passing through less than } k \text{ intermediate nodes.} \tag{7.8}$$

Then for $k = 1$ we pass directly from i to N and

$$f_1(i) = t_{iN}. \tag{7.9}$$

Again the principle of optimality gives

$$f_k(k) = \text{Min}\, \{t_{ij} + f_{k-1}(j)\}, \tag{7.10}$$

where the minimization is by correct choice of j. This includes the possibility of $j = 1$, for the optimal path from i to N with less than k intermediate nodes may in fact be the same as the optimal path with fewer than $(k - 1)$ nodes. When this happens for $i = 1$ for the first time we have the solution to the problem.

Another way to look at this solution is to regard it as an iterative procedure for solving equation (7.6). If $f_k(i)$ is the kth iteration defined by equations (7.9) and (7.10) then $f_k(i)$ is a decreasing sequence tending to a lower bound, T_i, which indeed it reaches in a finite number of iterations. A number of other methods of solution are given by Kalaba in the reference given at the end of this chapter (Bibliography 7.3).

7.4. Next best policies

It is sometimes of importance to determine the best alternative to an optimal policy, for if a particular link of the optimal route became impossible communication could only be maintained by switching to an alternative and this should be the best one available. Let us define Min_1 ( ) to mean the least value of the quantity which follows it and Min_2 ( ) as the second least value. Let S_i be the second least time from node i to node N. It must either be a combination of passage to the most suitable node j and the second best route thereafter, or of passage to the second most suitable node and optimal route thereafter. It is moreover the lesser of these for then it can only be bettered by the optimal route from i to N. Expressing this as a functional equation we have

$$S_i = \mathrm{Min}\,\{\mathrm{Min}_1\,(t_{ij} + S_j),\ \mathrm{Min}_2\,(t_{ij} + T_j)\}. \tag{7.11}$$

The solution of these equations depends on a knowledge of the optimal times T_j and is again a set of simultaneous, rather than recursive, equations.

As before, we can let $g_k(i)$ be the second shortest route with fewer than k intermediate nodes. Then

$$g_k(i) = \mathrm{Min}\,\{\mathrm{Min}_1\,[t_{ij} + g_{k-1}(j)],\ \mathrm{Min}_2\,[t_{ij} + f_{k-1}(j)]\} \tag{7.12}$$

provides an iterative scheme for approaching the solution.

Bibliography

7.1. Extensive references are given in:

BELLMAN, R., *Adaptive Control Processes* (Bibliography 1.8), Chapter 17.

7.3. A good review of network problems is given in

KALABA, R., "On Some Communication Network Problems," *Proc. Symp. Appl. Math.* (Amer. Math. Soc.), **10** (1960).

See also references in:

BELLMAN, R., and DREYFUS, S., *Applied Dynamic Programming* (Bibliography 1.8), Chapter 6.

An application of the network problem to control is given in:

ROBERTS, S. M., and MAHONEY, J. D., "Dynamic Programming Control of a Batch Reactor." *Chem. Eng. Prog.*, **58** (1962), 1. *Symp. Ser.*, **37**.

7.4. For a more extensive treatment of this question see

BELLMAN, R., and KALABA, R., "On k^{th} Best Policies." *J. Soc. Ind. Appl. Math.*, **8** (1960), 582.

Problems

1. Use the algorithm of section 7.3 to find the shortest path from the bottom left to the top right-hand corner of the following network.

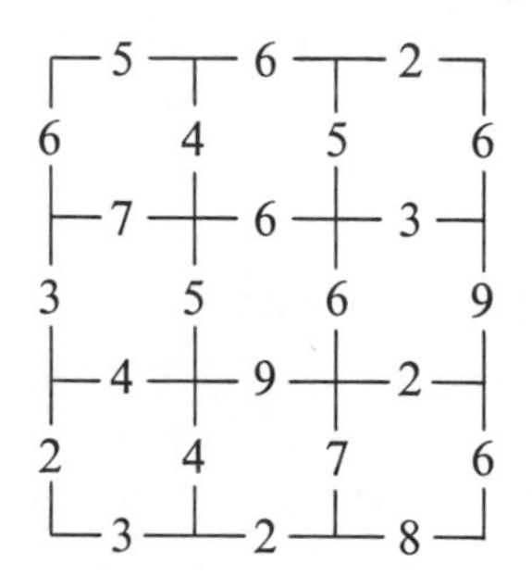

2. Find the second shortest path.
3. Let a_{ij} be a positive number and the ijth element of a matrix of order $N \times N$. The permanent of this matrix is the sum of products $a_{1i}a_{2j} \cdots a_{Nk}$ where $ij \cdots k$ is a permutation of $1, 2, \cdots, N$. Show how to find the greatest term in this sum. Hint: define $f_m(n_1, \cdots, n_{N-m})$ to be the largest product $a_{1i}a_{2j} \cdots a_{mk}$ where none of the $i, j, \cdots, k$ is any of the $n_1, \cdots, n_{N-m}$.
4. This algorithm seems to start with a function of $(N - 1)$ variables. Show that it can be regarded as a function of a single variable with N values. How many values does the corresponding f_m have?
5. Outline the development of this algorithm that would order the terms in the permanent in descending order of magnitude.

CHAPTER 8

Miscellaneous problems

In this chapter we shall gather together a few problems from rather diverse areas and go into them less deeply than before. The reader should now be thoroughly familiar with the principle of optimality and the way in which it is applied; this survey is aimed principally at showing the wide variety of topics that are touched by the notions of dynamic programming.

8.1. Fitting a curve with line segments

In analog computation it is common practice to simulate a function by a set of straight line segments, and it is interesting to find out how they should be chosen to give a fit that is in some sense the best. We will use the most popular of fits, namely, that which minimizes the integral of the squared deviation of the approximating segments from the curve.

Let the curve be given by the equation $y = f(x)$ and the range of interest be $a \leqslant x \leqslant b$. If we were to approximate it by only one segment $y = mx + c$ the deviation between the curve and the line would be $(f(x) - mx - c)$. The slope and intercept must therefore be chosen to minimize

$$F(m, c) = \int_a^b (f(x) - mx - c)^2 \, dx. \tag{8.1}$$

This minimum is easily found by noting that the integral is a continuous function of m and c and these are unrestricted variables. Thus the minimum occurs where the two partial derivatives vanish, and this gives

$$-\frac{1}{2}\frac{\partial F}{\partial m} = \int_a^b x(f(x) - mx - c) \, dx = 0, \tag{8.2}$$

$$-\frac{1}{2}\frac{\partial F}{\partial c} = \int_a^b (f(x) - mx - c) \, dx = 0. \tag{8.3}$$

Let us introduce the abbreviations

$$I_0(a,b)=\int_a^b f(x)\,dx, \qquad I_1(a,b)=\int_a^b xf(x)\,dx, \qquad I_2(a,b)=\int_a^b [f(x)]^2\,dx, \tag{8.4}$$

$$J_1=(b-a), \qquad J_2=\tfrac{1}{2}(b^2-a^2), \qquad J_3=\tfrac{1}{3}(b^3-a^3),$$

$$J_4=J_1J_3-J_2^2=\tfrac{1}{12}(b-a)^4. \tag{8.5}$$

Then the equations (8.2) and (8.3) are

$$mJ_3+cJ_2=I_1, \tag{8.6}$$

$$mJ_2+cJ_1=I_0, \tag{8.7}$$

of which the solutions are

$$m=(J_1I_1-J_2I_0)/J_4, \tag{8.8}$$

$$c=(J_3I_0-J_2I_1)/J_4. \tag{8.9}$$

The resulting minimum of $F(m, c)$ is

$$\begin{aligned} L_1(a,b) &= I_2+m^2J_3+c^2J_1+2mcJ_2-2mI_1-2cI_0 \\ &= I_2-(I_1^2J_1-2I_0I_1J_2+I_0^2J_3)/J_4. \end{aligned} \tag{8.10}$$

In fitting more than one line to the curve we have to find the breakpoints of the lines as well as the slope and intercept of each line. Let x_n, $n=0, 1, \cdots,$ N be the breakpoints, where $a=x_{N+1}\leqslant x_N\leqslant\cdots\leqslant x_2\leqslant x_1=b$. Then we wish to find

$$L_N(a,b)=L_N(x_{N+1},x_1)=\text{Min}\sum_1^N\int_{x_{n+1}}^{x_n}[f(x)-m_nx-c_n]^2\,dx, \tag{8.11}$$

and the minimum is by correct choice of the $3N-1$ quantities m_n, c_n, $n=1,$ $\cdots, N$, x_n, $n=2,\cdots,N$. By the principle of optimality

$$L_N(x_{N+1},x_1)=\text{Min}\,\{L_1(x_{N+1},x_N)+L_{N-1}(x_N,x_1)\}, \tag{8.12}$$

where here the minimization involves only the choice of x_N. The m_n and c_n are given by equations (8.8) and (8.9) with the integral evaluated for x_{n+1} and x_n in place of a and b.

But this reveals an interesting property of the best line sequence. For regarding x_1 as fixed,

$$\frac{dL_{N-1}}{dx_N}=\frac{\partial L_{N-1}}{\partial x_N}+\sum_1^{N-1}\frac{\partial L_{N-1}}{\partial x_n}\frac{\partial x_n}{\partial x_N}+\sum_1^{N-1}\frac{\partial L_{N-1}}{\partial m_n}\frac{\partial m_n}{\partial x_N}+\sum_1^{N-1}\frac{\partial L_{N-1}}{\partial c_n}\frac{\partial c_n}{\partial x_N}$$

and all except the first term vanish since the x_n, m_n, and c_n have been chosen to make the derivatives of L_{N-1} with respect to them zero. For the same reason, with fixed x_{N+1}, $dL_1/dx_N = \partial L_1/\partial x_N$ and so differentiating the expression on the right-hand side of equation (8.12) we have

$$\frac{\partial L_1}{\partial x_N} + \frac{\partial L_{N-1}}{\partial x_N} = [f(x_N) - m_N x_N - c_N]^2 - [f(x_N) - m_{N-1}x_N - c_N]^2 = 0.$$

Hence either

$$m_N x_N + c_N = m_{N-1}x_N + c_{N-1} \tag{8.13}$$

or

$$f(x_N) = \tfrac{1}{2}\{m_N x_N + c_N + m_{N-1}x_N + c_{N-1}\}. \tag{8.14}$$

The first equation means that the lines have the same ordinate at the breakpoint, the second that when the line segments are not continuous they are

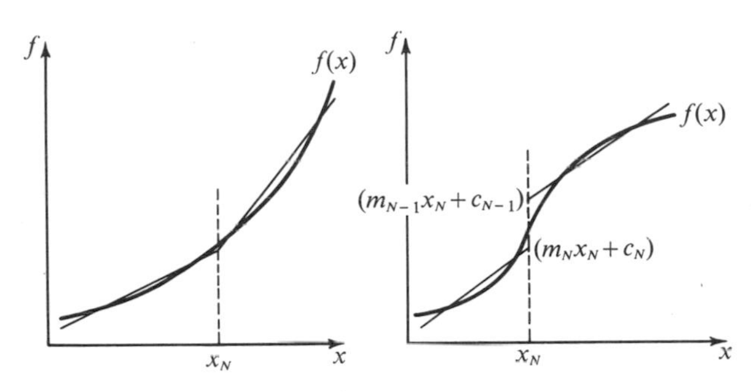

Figure 8.1

equidistant from the value of f at the breakpoint. It is easy to see as in Figure 8.1 that the second alternative is likely to occur near an inflexion point.

The results of the calculations could be conveniently represented by a set of double-entry tables. We might start with $L_1(a, b)$, and

$$y_*(a, b) = ma + c$$

and

$$y^*(a, b) = mb + c$$

calculated with m and c from (8.8) and (8.9). In fact,

$$y_*(a, b) = 6\{\tfrac{1}{3}(a + 2b)I_0 - I_1\}/(b - a)^2, \tag{8.15}$$

$$y^*(a, b) = 6\{I_1 - \tfrac{1}{3}(2a + b)I_0\}/(b - a)^2. \tag{8.16}$$

For a two-line fit we would have a breakpoint $x_1(a, b)$, where either

$$y^*(a, x_1) = y_*(x_1, b)$$

or

$$\tfrac{1}{2}\{y^*(a, x_1) + y_*(x_1, b)\} = f(x_1).$$

A table for $L_2(a, b)$ could then be calculated. For the three-line fit all that is needed is a table of $x_2(a, b)$ such that $y^*(a, x_2) = y_*[x_2, x_1(x_2, b)]$ or $\frac{1}{2}\{y^*(a, x_2) + y_*[x_2, x_1(x_2, b)]\} = f(x_2)$.

From tables of $L_n(a, b)$, $x_n(a, b)$, $y_*(a, b)$, and $y^*(a, b)$, $n = 1, \cdots, N$ the complete N-line best fit could be determined as follows. The end points a and b are given and N is chosen so that $L_N(a, b)$ is tolerably small. From the (a, b) entry in the table for $x_{N-1}(a, b)$ we find x_{N-1} and the line is fixed by the ordinates of the two end points $y_*(a, x_{N-1})$ and $y^*(a, x_{N-1})$. From the (x_{N-1}, b) entry in the table for x_{N-1} we have the next breakpoint and $y_*(x_{N-1}, x_{N-2})$, $y^*(x_{N-1}, x_{N-2})$ are the ordinates of its ends. An immediate check is that

$$y_*(x_{N-1}, x_{N+2}) = y^*(a, x_{N-1})$$

or

$$f(x_{N-1}) = \tfrac{1}{2}\{y^*(a, x_{N-1}) + y_*(x_{N-1}, x_{N-2})\}.$$

In this way we may pass from segment to segment. A final check is $L_N(a, b) = \Sigma_1^N L_1(x_{n+1}, x_n)$.

If the function to be fitted is given only by a set of tabular values a similar method applies but now of course the integrals will only be given approximately. Other types of fit may be treated in an entirely similar manner, such as that which would minimize the maximum deviation of the curve from the line or would fit a polynomial in each segment.

8.2. Some questions in reliability theory

Many questions in the theory of the reliability of multicomponent systems can be resolved by dynamic programming. Rudd has considered some chemical engineering systems, Bellman has given electronic overtones to his examples, and Kalaba a structural problem appropriate to the space age. To broaden our appeal let us consider Kalaba's example of designing a structure of minimum weight with given reliability. The structure consists of N elements the nth of which may be given a cross-sectional area A_n. The probability that this element will *not* fail is $p_n(A_n)$, where the form of the probability function depends on the shape of the element and its position in the structure. (Hilton and Feigen have given formulas for these under certain assumptions in the reference at the end of the chapter.) If the failure of any one element implies the failure of the whole structure and these failures are independent of one another the probability that the whole structure will *not* fail is

$$P_N = \prod_1^N p_n(A_n). \tag{8.17}$$

If w_n is the superficial density of the nth element so that its weight is w_nA_n we wish to minimize the total weight $\Sigma_1^N w_nA_n$ and not allow the probability P_N to drop below a certain value.

We may do this by adding one new element at a time and defining

$$f_N(p) = \text{Min} \sum_1^N w_nA_n \tag{8.18}$$

with $P_N \geqslant p$. For one element $N = 1$ we have

$$f_1(p) = w_1A_1 \tag{8.19}$$

where A_1 is found from the equation

$$P_1 = p_1(A_1) = p. \tag{8.20}$$

This is possible if $p_n(A_n)$ is a monotone increasing function of A_n as it is very reasonable to suppose. In the combination of two elements we can choose any value for A_2 and obtain a probability $p_2(A_2)$ that this element should not fail. With this choice of A_2 the probability that the first element must not fail is $p_1 = p/p_2$ and the minimum weight for the element therefore $f_1(p/p_2)$. Thus

$$f_2(p) = \underset{A_2}{\text{Min}} \{w_2A_2 + f_1[p/p_2(A_2)]\}. \tag{8.21}$$

In general

$$f_N(p) = \underset{A_N}{\text{Min}} \{w_NA_N + f_{N-1}[p/p_N(A_N)]\}. \tag{8.22}$$

A slightly different form of problem is obtained if we seek to maximize the reliability subject to certain limitations, say of weight and cost. Suppose W_{N+1} is the total weight available for N structural elements so that if A_N be chosen W_N, the available weight remaining is $W_{N+1} - w_NA_N$. Likewise $c_n(A_n)$ is the cost of the nth element, so that if C_{N+1} is the total amount of money available for N members, $C_N = C_{N+1} - c_N(A_N)$. We can formulate the problem in standard fashion as follows:

(i) State: W_n, C_n.
(ii) Decision: A_n.
(iii) Transformation: $W_n = W_{n+1} - w_nA_n$, $C_n = C_{n+1} - c_n(A_n)$.
(iv) Constraints: $A_n \geqslant 0$, $0 \leqslant W_n \leqslant W$, $0 \leqslant C_n \leqslant C$.
(v) Objective function: Maximize $\Pi_1^N p_n(A_n)$.
(vi) Parameters: w_n and parameters in $c_n(A_N)$.

Then if

$$f_N(W_{N+1}, C_{N+1}) = \text{Max} \prod_1^N p_n(A_n), \tag{8.23}$$

the principle of optimality gives

$$f_N(W_{N+1}, C_{N+1}) = \operatorname*{Max}_{A_N} p_N(A_N) f_{N-1}(W_N, C_N). \tag{8.24}$$

To avoid functions of two variables we might introduce a Lagrange multiplier and use only one state variable, say C_n. Thus if

$$g_N(C_{N+1}) = \text{Max} \prod_1^N [p_n(A_n) \exp - \lambda w_n A_n], \tag{8.25}$$

we would have

$$g_N(C_{N+1}) = \text{Max}\, \{p_N(A_N) e^{-\lambda w_N A_N}\, g_{N-1}(C_N)\}. \tag{8.26}$$

Bellman and Rudd have considered the optimal replication of components or operations in each stage to minimize the probability of failure subject to a certain cost or weight limitation.

8.3. Growth and predation

Some models of bacterial growth and competition have been formulated recently and promise interesting investigation. They have something in common with the bottleneck problem mentioned earlier but present rather greater difficulties of solution. We shall describe one briefly here to show that time (that is, the number of stages remaining) may not be the most suitable variable.

A nutrient X is required by two forms of an organism Y and Z if they are to remain viable. Y is not capable of reproduction but Z is and Y changes into Z by a first-order process. Besides reproducing itself Z may be expended to form a product P and this product enhances the reproductive process. If a small letter denotes the concentration or quantity of the species denoted by its capital and a suffix n the value of any quantity at the end of the time interval $n\,\Delta t$, $(n - 1)\,\Delta t$, (time being reckoned from the end of the process as usual) the equations are:

(i) the spontaneous change from Y to Z

$$\Delta y = -k_1 y_n\, \Delta t, \tag{8.27}$$

(ii) the formation of Z from Y, the reproduction of a fraction $(1 - \lambda_n)$ of itself and the use of the remaining fraction λ_n to form P,

$$\Delta z = k_1 y_n\, \Delta t + (1 - \lambda_n) m_n z_n\, \Delta t - \lambda_n k_2 z_n\, \Delta t, \tag{8.28}$$

(iii) the formation of P and its use to affect the reproduction constant m_n

$$\Delta p = \lambda_n k_2 z_n\, \Delta t - k_3 p_n\, \Delta t \tag{8.29}$$

(iv) the effect on the reproduction constant m_n

$$\Delta m = k_3 p_n \,\Delta t \tag{8.30}$$

(v) the use of the nutrient X to maintain the life of Y and Z,

$$\Delta x = -(k_4 y_n + k_5 z_n)\,\Delta t. \tag{8.31}$$

The $k_1, \cdots, k_5$ are a set of constants, and Δ denotes the change over an interval of time; for example, $\Delta x = x_{n-1} - x_n$.

The objective is to see how λ_n should be chosen to maximize the final concentration of Z. There is clearly a nice balance here for if λ is small the reproduction constant m remains small but if it is too large then too much effort is put into enhancing the reproductive process and too little Z is left to reproduce. However, what we mean by finality here can only be the exhaustion of the nutrient for a biological process is unlikely to have any other goal built into it. It is therefore more natural to use intervals of nutrient concentration rather than of time.

Let a suffix r denote the value of a quantity when $(r - 1)$ units of X remain and let us rewrite the equations by dividing each by the last and taking $\Delta x = -1$. Then

$$y_{r-1} = y_r - k_1 y_r/(k_4 y_r + k_5 z_r), \tag{8.32}$$

$$z_{r-1} = z_r + (k_1 y_r - (1 - \lambda_r) m_r + \lambda_r k_2 z_r)/(k_4 y_r + k_5 z_r), \tag{8.33}$$

$$p_{r-1} = p_r + (\lambda_r k_2 z_r - k_3 p_r)/(k_4 y_r + k_5 z_r), \tag{8.34}$$

$$m_{r-1} = m_r + k_3 p_r/(k_4 y_r + k_5 z_r). \tag{8.35}$$

The problem may now be formulated as follows:

(i) State: y_r, z_r, p_r, m_r.

(ii) Decision: λ_r.

(iii) Transformation: Equations (8.32)–(8.35).

(iv) Constraints: $0 \leqslant \lambda_r \leqslant 1$, y_r, z_r, p_r, m_r all $\geqslant 0$.

(v) Objective function: Maximize z_1.

(vi) Parameters: Any four independent ratios of $k_1, \cdots, k_5$.

If

$$f_R(y_{R+1}, z_{R+1}, p_{R+1}, m_{R+1}) = \operatorname*{Max}_{\{\lambda_r\}} [z_1], \tag{8.36}$$

then

$$f_R(y_{R+1}, z_{R+1}, p_{R+1}, m_{R+1}) = \operatorname*{Max}_{\lambda_R} [f_{R-1}(y_R, z_R, p_R, m_R)], \tag{8.37}$$

where in the second case only λ_R has to be chosen. The total quantity of nutrient at the start of the process is R units, and the process ends in a finite time with the exhaustion of this supply. It is clear that the dimensionality of this problem is too high for straightforward solution and further ways of using the special structure of the problem must be sought.

Bellman and Kalaba have considered a problem in population control of rather simpler structure which is worth mentioning. A population of creatures X preys on a population Y and both classes are undesirable. A pesticide is effective against X but not against Y and we face the problem of administering it with sufficient care that the population Y does not get out of hand through the diminution of its predators. If x_{n+1} is the population of X at n intervals of time before the end of the treatment and y_{n+1} the population of Y, the growth and predation can be represented by

$$x_n - x_{n+1} = \alpha x_{n+1} \tag{8.38}$$

$$y_n - y_{n+1} = -\beta x_{n+1} + \gamma y_{n+1}. \tag{8.39}$$

Now α, β, and γ are functions of the dosage of the pesticide, z_n. In particular $\alpha(z)$ becomes negative for sufficiently large z and $\beta(z)$ is diminished in that the effect of the drug may be to lessen the predation. If Y is truly unaffected γ will be constant, but for generality it may be regarded as a function of z_n. As a measure of control we might take a linear combination of the two populations, $ax_1 + by_1$, the weights a and b being measures of the objectionableness of X and Y. We then have:

(i) State: x_n, y_n.
(ii) Decision: z_n.
(iii) Transformation: $x_n = \{1 + \alpha(z_n)\}x_{n+1}$
$$y_n = -\beta(z_n)x_{n+1} + \{1 + \gamma(z_n)\}y_{n+1}.$$
(iv) Constraints: x_n, y_n, z_n positive.
(v) Objective function: Minimize $[ax_1 + by_1]$.
(vi) Parameters: a, b and those involved in α, β, and γ.

If

$$f_N(x_{N+1}, y_{N+1}) = \text{Min}\,(ax_1 + by_1) \tag{8.40}$$

is achieved by the optimal choice of $z_N, z_{N-1}, \cdots, z_1$, then

$$f_N(x_{N+1}, y_{N+1}) = \text{Min}\,[f_{N-1}(x_N, y_N)], \tag{8.41}$$

where now only z_N has to be chosen. We observe that the linearity of the equations can be exploited to reduce the dimensionality.

An interesting variant of this problem occurs if the control can only be exercised seasonally. Here z_n can only be chosen for $n = 1, 2, \cdots, k, L, L + 1, \cdots, L + k - 1, 2L, 2L + 1, \cdots$, where k is the number of intervals in a season and L the number between the beginning of two consecutive seasons. Here a steady rhythm can be built up which is in some sense optimal.

8.4. Jacobi matrices

To take a purely mathematical result consider the following example of Bellman's in matrix theory. A matrix with only diagonal, superdiagonal, and subdiagonal elements is called a Jacobi matrix. That is,

$$\mathbf{A}\colon a_{ij} = 0 \quad \text{unless} \quad |i - j| \leqslant 1. \tag{8.42}$$

The quadratic form $x'Ax$ associated with a positive definite symmetric Jacobi matrix of order N is

$$a_{11}x_1^2 + 2a_{12}x_1x_2 + a_{22}x_2^2 + \cdots + a_{N-1,\,N-1}x_{N-1}^2 + 2a_{N-1,\,N}x_{N-1}x_N + a_{NN}x_N^2. \tag{8.43}$$

If we form the nonhomogeneous quadratic expression

$$Q = \mathbf{x}'\mathbf{A}\mathbf{x} - \mathbf{c}'\mathbf{x} \tag{8.44}$$

and look for its minimum we have by straightforward differentiation that this occurs when $\mathbf{x}$ satisfies the equations

$$\mathbf{A}\mathbf{x} = \mathbf{c}. \tag{8.45}$$

It follows that if we can find the minimum by some other means the set of minimizing x_n is the solution of the equation. For Jacobi matrices this turns out to be quite simple.

Let us write the quadratic Q_N in N variables with the following grouping of terms:

$$\begin{aligned} Q_N = \{&a_{11}x_1^2 + 2a_{12}x_1x_2 + a_{22}x_2^2 + \cdots + 2a_{N-2,\,N-1}x_{N-2}x_{N-1} + a_{N-1,\,N-1}x_{N-1}^2 \\ &- 2(c_1x_1 + \cdots + c_{N-2}x_{N-2})\} \qquad\qquad (8.46) \\ &- \{2(c_{N-1} - a_{N-1,\,N}x_N)x_{N-1}\} + \{a_{NN}x_N^2 - 2c_Nx_N\}. \end{aligned}$$

The terms in the first bracket are those of Q_{N-1} with the exception of $-2c_{N-1}x_{N-1}$, which has been combined with the only other term in x_{N-1}; the final bracket consists in all the terms in x_N only. Evidently the second bracket provides a link between the Q_N and Q_{N-1} and suggests writing

$$\begin{aligned} Q_{N-1}(x; z) = Q_{N-1}(x_1, \cdots, x_{N-1}; z) = a_{11}x_1^2 + 2a_{12}x_1x_2 + \cdots + a_{N-1,\,N-1}x_{N-1}^2 \\ - 2c_1x_1 - \cdots - 2c_{N-2}x_{N-2} - 2zx_{N-1}. \end{aligned}$$

Then Q_{N-1} is $Q_{N-1}(x;\, c_{N-1})$ and from equation (8.46) above (with $c_N = z$)

$$Q_N(x;\, z) = Q_{N-1}(x;\, c_{N-1} - a_{N-1,N}x_N) + a_{NN}x_N^2 - 2zx_N. \tag{8.47}$$

The value of writing the expression in this way is that now all the variables $x_1, \cdots, x_{N-1}$ are contained in the first expression.

Now let

$$f_N(z) = \text{Min } Q_N(x; z), \tag{8.48}$$

where the minimization involves the choice of $x_1, \cdots, x_N$. From equation (8.47) and the principle of optimality we have

$$f_N(z) = \text{Min } \{a_{NN}x_N^2 - 2zx_N + f_{N-1}(c_{N-1} - a_{N-1,N}x_N)\}, \tag{8.49}$$

where now only x_N has to be chosen. In particular

$$f_1(z) = \text{Min } (a_{11}x_1^2 - 2zx_1) = -z^2/a_{11} \tag{8.50}$$

and is attained when

$$x_1 = z/a_{11}. \tag{8.51}$$

Substituting in equation (8.49) with $N = 2$,

$$f_2(z) = \text{Min } [a_{22}x_2^2 - 2zx_2 - (c_1 - a_{12}x_2)^2/a_{11}]$$

$$= \text{Min } \left[\frac{a_{11}a_{22} - a_{12}^2}{a_{11}} x_2^2 - 2(z - a_{12}c_1/a_{11})x_2 - c_1^2/a_{11}\right].$$

Hence

$$x_2 = (a_{11}z - a_{12}c_1)/(a_{11}a_{22} - a_{12}^2), \tag{8.52}$$

and

$$f_2(z) = -\{a_{11}z^2 - 2c_1a_{12}z + c_1^2a_{22}\}/\{a_{11}a_{22} - a_{12}^2\}. \tag{8.53}$$

We observe that f_2 is a quadratic form in z and by deliberately writing f_N as a quadratic form and equating coefficients in equation (8.49) we have the following recurrence relations:

$$f_N(z) = -\alpha_N z^2 + 2\beta_N z - \gamma_N, \tag{8.54}$$

where

$$\Delta_N = a_{NN} - \alpha_{N-1}a_{N-1,N}^2 \tag{8.55}$$

$$\alpha_N = 1/\Delta_N \tag{8.56}$$

$$\beta_N = \{\alpha_{N-1}c_{N-1} - \beta_{N-1}\}/\Delta_N \tag{8.57}$$

$$\gamma_N = \{a_{NN}(\alpha_{N-1}c_{N-1}^2 - 2\beta_{N-1}c_{N-1} + \gamma_{N-1}) + a_{N-1,N}^2(\beta_{N-1}^2 - \alpha_{N-1}\gamma_{N-1})\}/\Delta_N \tag{8.58}$$

and

$$x_N = \{z - (\alpha_{N-1}c_{N-1} - \beta_{N-1})\}/\Delta_N. \tag{8.59}$$

These recurrence relations are not particularly elegant but they provide a complete computational solution.

Bibliography

8.1. See also:

BELLMAN, R., "On the Approximation of Curves by Line Segments Using Dynamic Programming," *Comm. of the Assoc. for Computing Machinery*, **4** (1961), 294.

BELLMAN, R., and KOTKIN, B., "On the Approximation of Curves by Line Segments Using Dynamic Programming," RAND Corporation Memo RM-2978-PR, The RAND Corporation, February, 1962.

BELLMAN, R., and DREYFUS, S. E., *Applied Dynamic Programming* (Bibliography 1.8), p. 334.

FRYER, W. D., "Best Approximation in the Chebyshev Sense of *N* Line Segments to a Curve by Means of Dynamic Programming." Paper presented at an annual meeting of SIAM, 1962.

8.2. BELLMAN, R., and DREYFUS, S., "Dynamic Programming and the Reliability Theory of Multicomponent Devices," *Operations Res.*, **6** (1958), 200.

BELLMAN, R., and DREYFUS, S. E., *Applied Dynamic Programming* (Bibliography 1.8), p. 33–34, 65–69.

RUDD, D. F., "Reliability Theory in Chemical System Design," *Ind. Eng. Chem. Fundamentals*, **1** (1962), 138.

KALABA, R., "Design of Minimal Weight Structures for Given Reliability and Cost," *J. Aerospace Sci.*, **29** (1962), 355.

HILTON, H., and FEIGEN, M., "Minimum Weight Analysis Based on Structural Reliability," *J. Aerospace Sci.*, **27** (1960), 641.

8.3. BELLMAN, R., and KALABA, R., "Some Mathematical Aspects of Optimal Predation in Ecology and Boviculture," *Proc. Nat. Acad. Sci. U.S.*, **46** (1960), 718.

8.4. BELLMAN, R., *Introduction to Matrix Analysis*. New York: McGraw-Hill Book Co., Inc., 1960. Chapter 9.

The following is a list of some others of the diverse applications that have been made of dynamic programming. It makes no pretense to be complete (see Preface).

To allocation of water resources:

HALL, W. A., and BURAS, N., "The Dynamic Programming Approach to Water Resources Development," *J. Geophys. Res.*, **66** (1961), 517.

To some classic fireside problems:

BELLMAN, R., "Dynamic Programming and 'Difficult Crossing' Puzzles." *Math. Mag.*, **35** (1962).

See also BELLMAN, *Applied Dynamic Programming* (Bibliography 1.8), Chapter 2.

To interplanetary flight:

BELLMAN R., and DREYFUS, S., "An Application of Dynamic Programming to the Determination o Optimal Satellite Trajectories," *J. Brit. Interplanet. Soc.*, **17** (1959), 78.

TEN-DYKE, R. P., "Computation of Rocket Step Weights to Minimize Initial Gross Weights." *Jet Propulsion*, **28** (1958), 338.

See also articles by Bellman and Kalaba in *Optimization Techniques with Applications to Aerospace Systems*, Edited by G. Leitmann. New York: Academic Press, Inc., 1962.

To chemical engineering problems:

RUDD, D., "On Design Policies for the Optimal Use of Limited Resources." *Chem. Eng. Sci.*, **17** (1962), 609.

GRÜTTER, W. F., and MESSIKOMMER, B. H., "Dynamische Programmierung in der chemischen Technik. Die Optimierung chemischer Reaktionausbeuten." *Helv. Chim. Acta.*, **43** (1960), 2182.

ROBERTS, S. M., "Dynamic Programming Formulation of the Catalyst Replacement Problem." *Chem. Eng. Prog.*, **56** (1960), 103. *Symp. Ser.* **31**.

WESTBROOK, G. T., "Use This Method to Size Each Stage for Best Operation." Petrol. Refiner, **40** (1961), 201.

ARIS, R., BELLMAN, R., and KALABA, R., "Some Optimization Problems in Chemical Engineering." *Chem. Eng. Prog.*, **56** (1960), 95. *Symp. Ser.* **31**.

To forestry:

ARIMIZU, T., "Working Group Matrix in Dynamic Model of Forest Management," *J. Japan. Forestry Soc.*, **40** (1958), 185.

To nuclear engineering:

ASH, M., BELLMAN, R., and KALABA, R., "On Control of Reactor Shutdown Involving Minimal Xenon Poisoning." *Nucl. Sci. Eng.*, **6** (1959), 152.

To a class of adaptive control processes:

BELLMAN, R., and KALABA, R., "Dynamic Programming and Adaptive Control Processes: Mathematical Foundations," *IRE, Trans. Auto. Control AC*–**5** (1960), 5.

Problems

1. If $f(x) = x^2$ show that

$$L_1(a, b) = \min_{m,c} \int_a^b (x^2 - mx - c)^2 \, dx$$

$$= (b - a)^5 L_1(0, 1).$$

   Hint: use change of variable $x = a + (b - a)y$.

2. Deduce that $L_N(a, b) = (b - a)^5 L_N(0, 1)$ and hence that $L_{2N}(a, b) = (b - a)^5 L_N(0,1)/16$.

3. Use a similar reasoning on $f(x) = e^{-cx}$ to show that

$$L_N(a, b) = e^{-ac} L_N(0, b - a)$$

   and hence that

$$L_{2N}(0, b) = \min_z [L_N(0, z) + e^{-cz} L_N(0, b - z)].$$

4. A chemical product P is produced in three intermediate steps from the raw material R: $R + A \to B$, $B + C \to D$, $D + E \to P$. Of these, R is cheap but the costs of the reagents A, C, and E are \$5, 5, 1 per batch, respectively; the value of a batch of the product is \$50. Unfortunately the processes for preparing them are not reliable and their probabilities of success are $\frac{3}{4}$, $\frac{1}{2}$, $\frac{1}{3}$, respectively. Show that to maximize the expected profit 7 batches of A, 3 batches of C, and 2 of E should be prepared. (Rudd.)

CHAPTER 9

Connections between the continuous and the discrete

This book is concerned primarily with discrete dynamic programming, where the process is described by difference equations and the decisions have to be made at each stage. There is an extensive area of interest that can be explored by dynamic programming in which the process is continuous and the decision variables have to be chosen continuously. This area, which we have glanced at in Chapter 1, was originally discovered by the methods of the calculus of variations and is still a region of the liveliest research. The interrelation of the different methods of approach is illuminating and involves some quite subtle questions still under discussion. Most of this is outwith our present policies, but it is of importance to explore some of the connections between the continuous and the discrete. In particular since a continuous process can be sampled at discrete intervals we may treat this type of control of continuous systems by discrete methods. Let us turn first, however, to the limit of a process with a large number of small stages.

9.1. The continuous as the limit of the discrete

As an elementary example of the approach to the continuous limit let us look back at the continuous stirred-reactor system described in detail in the beginning of Chapter 2. This time we will take the holding times θ_n of each stage to be the same, say θ, and ask for the sequence of temperatures T_n that will maximize the final extent of reaction. The equations of transformation, which are the same as (4.1), are

$$c_n = c_{n+1} + \theta\{k_1(T_n)(1 - c_n) - k_2(T_n)c_n\}, \tag{9.1}$$

with $k_1(T\}$ and $k_2(T)$ the usual Arrhenius functions. A problem can then be formulated as follows:

(i) State: c_n.
(ii) Decision: T_n.
(iii) Transformation: $c_n = \{c_{n+1} + \theta k_1(T_n)\}/\{k_1(T_n) + k_2(T_n)\}$.
(iv) Constraints: $T_* \leqslant T_n \leqslant T^*$, $c_n \geqslant 0$.
(v) Objective function: Maximize $c_1 - c_{N+1} = \Sigma_1^N(c_{n+1} - c_n)$.
(vi) Parameters: θ.

If we set

$$f_N(c_{N+1}) = \text{Max} \sum_1^N (c_{n+1} - c_n) \tag{9.2}$$

then

$$f_N(c_{N+1}) = \text{Max} \{(c_{N+1} - c_N) + f_{N-1}(c_N)\} \tag{9.3}$$

where now only T_N has to be chosen. But, as we have seen before, T_N is always chosen to maximize the reaction rate, for the derivative of the quantity in the brackets is $-[1 - f'(c_N)]\partial(c_N - c_{N+1})/\partial T_N$, and this is zero when $T_N = T^0(c_N)$ (cf. p. 40).

Now let $t = N\theta$ be the total holding time of the sequence and let $N \to \infty$ and $\theta \to 0$, keeping t constant. Equation (9.1) can be written

$$\frac{c_{n+1} - c_n}{\theta} = -\{k_1(T_n)(1 - c_n) - k_2(T_n)c_n\}.$$

If $\tau = n\theta$ is the variable time, $0 \leqslant \tau \leqslant t$, $c_n = c(\tau)$ and $c_{n+1} = c(\tau + \theta)$. Hence $(c_{n+1} - c_n)/\theta = \{c(\tau + \theta) - c(\tau)\}/\theta$ and in the limit this $dc/d\tau$. Thus denoting $c(\tau)$ by c and $T(\tau)$ by T we have

$$\frac{dc}{d\tau} = -\{k_1(T)(1 - c) - k_2(T)c\}. \tag{9.4}$$

This differential equation replaces the difference equation (9.1). Similarly the objective function (9.2) can be written

$$f[c(t)] = \text{Max}\,\{c(0) - c(t)\} = \text{Max} \int_0^t \{k_1(T)(1 - c) - k_2(T)c\}\, d\tau \tag{9.5}$$

and this is the limit as $\theta \to 0$ of

$$f_N(c_{N+1}) = \text{Max}\,[c_1 - c_{N+1}] = \text{Max} \sum_1^N \{k_1(T_n)(1 - c_n) - k_2(T_n)c_n\}\theta.$$

The continuous problem would thus be stated as follows. Given the differential equation (9.4) for the state variable c as a function of τ, the time from the end of the process, determine the decision variables $T(\tau)$ for $0 \leqslant \tau \leqslant t$, so that with given $c(t)$ the conversion $c(0) - c(t)$ is maximized.

Turning to the general discrete process of section 2.3 we may make the following (purely formal) approach to a continuous process. The state vector $\mathbf{p}_n$ is replaced by a vector of functions $\mathbf{p} = [p_1(\tau), \cdots, p_s(\tau)]$, where $\tau = n\,\Delta t$, and the decision vector $\mathbf{q}_n$ by $\mathbf{q}(\tau) = [q_1(\tau), \cdots, q_r(\tau)]$. The transformation $\mathbf{p}_n = \mathscr{T}_n(\mathbf{p}_{n+1}; \mathbf{q}_n)$ can be written

$$\frac{\mathbf{p}_{n+1} - \mathbf{p}_n}{\Delta\tau} = -\frac{\mathscr{T}_n(\mathbf{p}_{n+1}; \mathbf{q}_n) - \mathbf{p}_{n+1}}{\Delta\tau}.$$

In the limit this becomes

$$\frac{d\mathbf{p}}{d\tau} = -\mathscr{U}(\mathbf{p}; \mathbf{q}; \tau) \tag{9.6}$$

where $\mathscr{U}$ is the limit of the right-hand side. Similarly P_n, the marginal profit from stage n, can be replaced by a function $P(\mathbf{p}; \mathbf{q}; \tau)\,\Delta\tau$. The factor of $\Delta\tau$ is necessary for we are considering $\Delta\tau \to 0$ and the marginal profit must ultimately be proportional to the size of the stage. Thus, if $t = N\,\Delta\tau$, the objective function is

$$\mathscr{O} = \int_0^t P(\mathbf{p}(\tau); \mathbf{q}(\tau); \tau)\,d\tau. \tag{9.7}$$

The restrictions would take the same form as in the discrete case

$$\mathscr{S}_m(\mathbf{p}(\tau); \mathbf{q}(\tau); \tau) \geqslant 0. \tag{9.8}$$

The analogy between this and the standard discrete problem format is worth recording.

(i) State: $\mathbf{p}(\tau)$, $0 \leqslant \tau \leqslant t$.
(ii) Decision: $\mathbf{q}(\tau)$, $0 \leqslant \tau \leqslant t$.
(iii) Transformation: $d\mathbf{p}/d\tau = -\mathscr{U}(\mathbf{p}; \mathbf{q}; \tau)$.
(iv) Constraints: $\mathscr{S}_m(\mathbf{p}; \mathbf{q}; \tau) \geqslant 0$, $m = 1, \cdots, l$
(v) Objective function: $\mathscr{O} = \int_0^t P(\mathbf{p}; \mathbf{q}; \tau)\,d\tau$.
(vi) Parameters.

9.2. The discrete as a sampling of the continuous

Let us now reverse the viewpoint and consider how a continuous system can be observed discretely. As usual we work back from the end of the process, which corresponds to a time $\tau = 0$, and this accounts for the negative sign we put into the equations. (Artificial though this seems, it does give a valuable consistency to the equations in the analysis of continuous systems.) Let the equations then be

$$\frac{d\mathbf{p}}{d\tau} = -\mathscr{U}(\mathbf{p}; \mathbf{q}; \tau), \tag{9.9}$$

which of course require a set of initial values before they can be integrated. The physically proper conditions are

$$\mathbf{p}(t) = \mathbf{p}_{N+1} \tag{9.10}$$

and the equations can be integrated from $\tau = t$ to $\tau = 0$ as soon as the decision vector $\mathbf{q}(\tau)$ is chosen. Suppose we consider that the interval $0 \leqslant \tau \leqslant t$ is divided into N (not necessarily equal) parts by a set of values $0 = \tau_1 \leqslant \tau_2 \leqslant \cdots \leqslant \tau_N \leqslant \tau_{N+1} = t$; then $\mathbf{p}(\tau_n)$ can be denoted by $\mathbf{p}_n$. Similarly if $\mathbf{q}_n$ denotes the choice of $\mathbf{q}(\tau)$ for $\tau_n \leqslant \tau \leqslant \tau_{n+1}$ (and this need not be a constant) we may integrate the equations from stage to stage. Thus as the result of integrating the equations (9.9) from τ_{N+1} to τ_N we have a solution that we may write

$$\mathbf{p}_N = \mathscr{T}_n(\mathbf{p}_{N+1}; \mathbf{q}_N) \tag{9.11}$$

and in general for the interval $\tau_n \leqslant \tau \leqslant \tau_{n+1}$,

$$\mathbf{p}_n = \mathscr{T}_n(\mathbf{p}_{n+1}; \mathbf{q}_n). \tag{9.12}$$

We have to put a suffix n on the function $\mathscr{T}$ for in general the equations (9.9) depend on τ. For autonomous systems, where $\mathscr{U}$ is a function of $\mathbf{p}$ and $\mathbf{q}$ only, the function $\mathscr{T}$ might be independent of n. Now the solution of a differential equation enjoys the semigroup property that the same result is obtained if the solution is found by integrating over the interval in two stages using the final values of the first stage as the initial values of the second. Thus $\mathbf{p}_1$ as calculated by the successive application of the transformation (9.12) is indeed the solution that would be obtained by integrating the equations over the whole interval.

Similarly an objective like (9.7) can be given discrete form by the same division of the total interval;

$$\begin{aligned} \mathscr{O} &= \int_0^t P(\mathbf{p}; \mathbf{q}; \tau)\, d\tau = \sum_1^N \int_{\tau_n}^{\tau_{n+1}} P(\mathbf{p}; \mathbf{q}; \tau)\, d\tau \\ &= \sum_1^N P_n(\mathbf{p}_{n+1}; \mathbf{q}_n) \end{aligned} \tag{9.13}$$

since the value of the integral for each stage can be calculated in terms of $\mathbf{p}_{n+1}$ and $\mathbf{q}_n$ by the integration of the equations (9.9).

To illustrate this we may consider the equation for a batch reactor in which the first-order reaction $A \rightleftharpoons B$ is taking place. This is in fact the equation (9.4) for it is the limit of a large number of small stages

$$\frac{dc}{d\tau} = -\{k_1(T)(1 - c) - k_2(T)c\}. \tag{9.14}$$

Let us choose to keep T constant during the interval $\tau_n \leqslant \tau \leqslant \tau_{n+1}$ and denote its value by T_n. Then integration of the first-order equation (9.14) gives

$$c_n = c_{n+1} \exp -[(k_{1n} + k_{2n})(\tau_{n+1} - \tau_n)]$$
$$+ k_{1n}\{1 - \exp -[(k_{1n} + k_{2n})(\tau_{n+1} - \tau_n)]\}/(k_{1n} + k_{2n}),$$

where $k_i(T_n) = k_{in}$. Notice that these are not the same as the equations for finite stirred tanks, for we are now dealing with the change over a finite interval of a different system. However, if $\tau_{n+1} - \tau_n = \theta$ is very small so that θ^2 and higher powers can be neglected, we recover the equations (9.1) by expanding the exponentials. If the objective were the maximization of $c(0) - c(t)$ we could write this immediately as $\Sigma_1^N P_n$, where $P_n = c_n - c_{n+1}$. Thus by specifying that the control should be such that T is constant over each interval we have obtained a discrete dynamic programming problem.

9.3. Programmed temperature control for a batch reactor

We will illustrate this process of discretization more fully by an example which is very close to that of Chapter 4. Given a batch reactor governed by the equations of the previous section, how do we choose a sequence of N temperatures T_n and the intervals (τ_n, τ_{n+1}) over which they should be exercised to get a conversion $c_1 = \gamma$ in the minimum time? Here the objective function is the total time

$$\mathcal{O} = \sum_1^N (\tau_{n+1} - \tau_n). \tag{9.15}$$

Now equation (9.14) can be written

$$\tau_{n+1} - \tau_n = \int_{\tau_n}^{\tau_{n+1}} d\tau = \int_{c_{n+1}}^{c_n} dc/\{k_{1n} - (k_{1n} + k_{2n})c\}$$
$$= \frac{1}{(k_{1n} + k_{2n})} \ln \frac{k_{1n} - (k_{1n} + k_{2n})c_{n+1}}{k_{1n} - (k_{1n} + k_{2n})c_n}. \tag{9.16}$$

If the conversion were obtained in one stage, that is, with $T_n = T_1$, the time required would be

$$t_2 = \tau_2 - \tau_1 = \frac{1}{k_{11} + k_{21}} \ln \frac{k_{11} - (k_{11} + k_{21})c_2}{k_{11} - (k_{11} + k_{21})c_1}. \tag{9.17}$$

The minimum value of this time will be given by some temperature T_1^0 which is a function of c_2 and $c_1 = \gamma$. In the two-stage problem we have to choose

T_2, T_1, τ_3, and τ_2, but since the requirement that $c_1 = \gamma$ must be met there are really only three quantities to be chosen. Again, because we have a closed formula for τ in terms of c, it is better to work with the intermediate extents $c_N, \cdots, c_2$ as the $(N - 1)$ decision variables.

The value of the temperature that minimizes the right-hand side of equation (9.16) may be denoted by $T^0(c_n, c_{n+1})$ and the corresponding minimum value of $\tau_{n+1} - \tau_n$ by $\Delta\tau_n^0$: $T^0(c_n, c_{n+1})$ is not unrelated to the temperature $T^0(c)$ that maximizes the reaction rate. In Figure 9.1 the curve Γ is the same as that

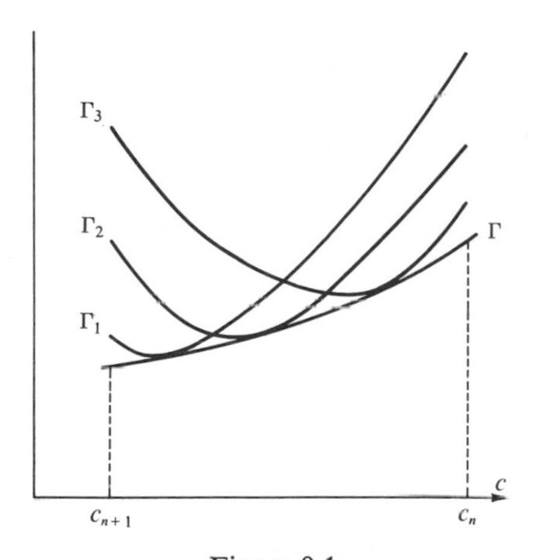

Figure 9.1

in Chapter 4, namely the curve given by the reciprocal of the reaction rate as a function of temperature, and it will be recalled that it would be graduated in $T^0(c)$: the curves Γ_1, Γ_2, Γ_3 are three typical curves given by the reciprocal reaction rate at three trial temperatures. It is the area under one of these curves that gives $(\tau_{n+1} - \tau_n)$ according to equation (9.16) and while this area will necessarily be greater than that under Γ there will be one such curve Γ_p that gives the minimum area. The graduation $T^0(c)$ at the point where this curve touches Γ is $T^0(c_n, c_{n+1})$. Thus $T^0(c_n, c_{n+1}) = T^0(c_n')$, where $c_{n+1} \leqslant c_n' \leqslant c_n$ and the optimal temperature corresponds to that which gives the maximum reaction rate at some intermediate extent. The function $T^0(c_n, c_{n+1})$ can be precalculated and hence $\Delta\tau^0(c_n, c_{n+1})$; then the problem is reduced to finding $c_N, \cdots, c_2$ such that $\Sigma_1^N \Delta\tau^0(c_n, c_{n+1})$ is least. The answer finally comes in the form of a program for the temperature control $T(\tau) = T_n$, $\tau_n \leqslant \tau \leqslant \tau_{n+1}$, giving both temperatures and switching times. The whole result can be presented in the same graphical style as in Chapter 4 and the details of this are left to the reader.

9.4. Linearization

A device in the discretization of continuous systems that is sometimes useful is a local linearization. By this device the numerical integration of a nonlinear autonomous equation is avoided at the cost of some accuracy of solution. Let us see how it leads to a matrix form of $\mathscr{T}_n$ from the differential equation.

The vector differential equation

$$\frac{d\mathbf{p}}{d\tau} = -\mathscr{U}(\mathbf{p}; \mathbf{q}) \tag{9.18}$$

is an abbreviation for the set of equations

$$\frac{dp_k}{d\tau} = -U_k(p_1, \cdots, p_s; q_1, \cdots, q_r), \qquad k = 1, \cdots, s. \tag{9.19}$$

If the values of $p_k(\tau_{n+1})$ are given and $\tau_{n+1} - \tau_n$ is not large we may expect that the values of $p_k(\tau)$ will not differ too much from the $p_{n+1,k} = p_k(\tau_{n+1})$. Then an approximation to the right-hand side of equation (9.19) is given by expanding it as a function of the differences $\pi_k(\tau) = p_k(\tau) - p_{n+1,k}$. In particular, by Taylor's theorem,

$$U_k(p_1, \cdots, p_s; \mathbf{q}) = U_k(p_{n+1,1}, \cdots, p_{n+1,s}; \mathbf{q}) + \sum_{j=1}^{s} \frac{\partial U_k}{\partial p_j}(p_{n+1,1}, \cdots, p_{n+1,s}; \mathbf{q})\pi_j(\tau)$$

where squares and products of the π_j have been discarded. The quantities on the right-hand side of this last equation can be calculated from the known $p_{n+1} = (p_{n+1,1}, \cdots, p_{n+1,s})$ as soon as decision vector q is chosen. Let

$$b_k^{(n)} = U_k(p_{n+1,1}, \cdots, p_{n+1,s}; \mathbf{q}_n),$$

and

$$a_{kj}^{(n)} = \frac{\partial U_k}{\partial p_j}(p_{n+1,1}, \cdots, p_{n+1,s}; \mathbf{q}_n). \tag{9.20}$$

Then the equations (9.19) read

$$\frac{d\pi_k}{d\tau} = -b_k^{(n)} - a_{kj}^{(n)}\pi_j \tag{9.21}$$

or in vector form

$$\frac{d\boldsymbol{\pi}}{d\tau} = -\mathbf{b}^{(n)} - \mathbf{A}^{(n)}\boldsymbol{\pi}, \tag{9.22}$$

where $A^{(n)}$ is the matrix with elements $a_{kj}^{(n)}$. These elements are constants calculated from the known initial vector $\mathbf{p}_{n+1}$ and the decision vector $\mathbf{q}_n$. Now the solution of the general linear equation is known in closed form and is entirely analogous to that for one variable. The solution of the equation

$$\frac{d\pi}{d\tau} = -b - A\pi, \tag{9.23}$$

where b and A are constants and $\pi(\tau)$ a single variable, and $\pi(0) = 0$, is

$$\pi(\tau) = -A^{-1}(1 - e^{-A\tau})b. \tag{9.24}$$

The exponential function can be defined by the power series

$$e^{-A\tau} = 1 - A\tau + \frac{1}{2'} A^2\tau^2 - \frac{1}{3'} A^3\tau^3 + \cdots.$$

By analogy the exponential function for a matrix is defined by the series

$$\exp -\mathbf{A}\tau = \sum_0^\infty \frac{\tau^p}{p!} \mathbf{A}^p, \tag{9.25}$$

where $\mathbf{A}^0$ is the identity matrix and $\mathbf{A}^n$ the product of n A's. It will be found that equation (9.22) is satisfied by

$$\boldsymbol{\pi}(\tau) = -[\mathbf{A}^{(n)}]^{-1}(I - \exp -\mathbf{A}^{(n)}\tau)\mathbf{b}^{(n)}. \tag{9.26}$$

Hence, when $\tau = \tau_n - \tau_{n+1}$ so that $\boldsymbol{\pi}(\tau) = \mathbf{p}_n - \mathbf{p}_{n+1}$, we have

$$\mathbf{p}_n - \mathbf{p}_{n+1} + [\mathbf{A}^{(n)}]^{1}\{\exp \mathbf{A}^{(n)}(\tau_{n+1} - \tau_n) - \mathbf{I}\}\mathbf{b}^{(n)}. \tag{9.27}$$

In that $\mathbf{A}^{(n)}$ and $\mathbf{b}^{(n)}$ are known functions of $\mathbf{p}_{n+1}$ and $\mathbf{q}_n$ we have here an explicit formula of the form $\mathbf{p}_n = \mathscr{T}_n(\mathbf{p}_{n+1}; \mathbf{q}_n)$.

Bibliography

A good exposition of the value of discretization in a chemical engineering problem is to be found in

LAPIDUS, L., KALMAN, R. E., and SHAPIRO, E., "Computer Control of Processes," *Chem. Eng. Prog.*, **56** (1960), 55.

For an excellent account of linear matrix differential equations see

BELLMAN, R., *Introduction to Matrix Analysis*. New York: McGraw-Hill Book Co., Inc., 1961.

A sophisticated treatment of piecewise linearization is given in

MAH, R. S. H., MICHAELSON, S., and SARGENT, R. W. H., "Dynamic Behaviour of Multi-component Multi-stage Systems. Numerical Methods for the Solution," *Chem. Eng. Sci.*, **17** (1962), 619.

Problems

1. A simplified form of the equations of motion of an airplane is

$$\frac{dH}{dt} = V \sin \theta,$$

$$\frac{1}{g}\frac{dV}{dt} = \frac{T - D}{W} - \sin \theta,$$

H is the height, V the velocity, T the thrust, D the drag, W the weight, and θ the angle of climb; T and D are functions of H and V.

Define $f(H, V)$ to be the minimum time to climb from height H with velocity V to some final specified height and velocity by optimal control of θ. Discretize the problem by taking H to have values $O, h, \cdots, Nh =$ final height and so develop a recursive equation. [A detailed treatment is given in Bellman, *Applied Dynamic Programming* (Bibliography 1.8), Chapter 6.]

2. Consider the problem of cooling a batch reactor by dumping in quantities of cold feed at a number of preassigned instants. Supplement the equations of section 9.3 to get a discrete problem.
3. Consider the stretching of an elastic cord with continuously varying elastic properties as the continuous limit in problem 10 of Chapter 3.
4. Consider the passage of the limit in problem 9 of Chapter 3.

CHAPTER 10

Some extensions and limitations

In Chapter 3 we were careful to restrict the application of dynamic programming to a straight chain process with no feedback. In this chapter we wish to explore this possibility applying our methods to feedback or counter-current systems. To show how carefully one must proceed let us first give an elementary example showing that the principle of optimality in its simplest form is not generally applicable to a system with feedback.

10.1. Counter-examples for feedback

Consider the two stage system shown in Figure 10.1, in which decision

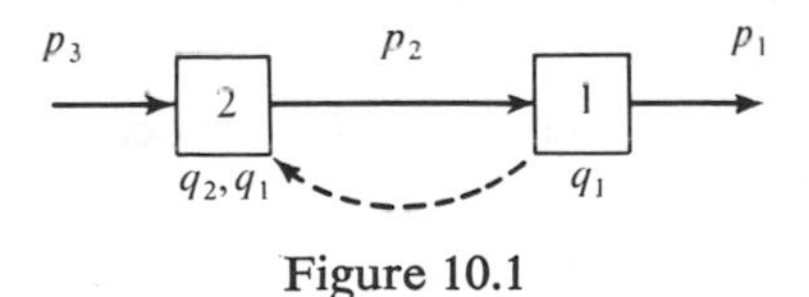

Figure 10.1

variable q_1 of stage 1 also affects the transformation of stage 2. We take the very simple transformations

$$p_1 = 2q_1p_2 - q_1^2, \tag{10.1}$$

$$p_2 = 2q_2(p_3 - \lambda q_1) - q_2^2, \tag{10.2}$$

with the objective of maximizing p_1.

Evidently if $\lambda = 0$ we have no feedback and in this case the optimal policy is $q_1 = p_2$, $q_2 = p_3$. But, since by equation (10.2) $p_2 = p_3^2$, the resulting maximum of p_1 would be $f_2(p_3) = p_3^4$. If feedback is present and $\lambda \neq 0$ then by substitution

$$p_1 = 4q_1q_2(p_3 - \lambda q_1) - 2q_1q_2^2 - q_1^2. \tag{10.3}$$

From this it follows that q_1 and q_2 must be chosen to satisfy

$$\begin{aligned} 2q_2p_3 - q_2^2 - q_1(1 + 4\lambda q_2) &= 0, \\ q_1(p_3 - \lambda q_1) - q_1q_2 &= 0. \end{aligned} \tag{10.4}$$

The principle of optimality will be violated if q_1 is not equal to p_2, for given p_2 this is certainly the value of q_1 that maximizes p_1. To show that this is not so

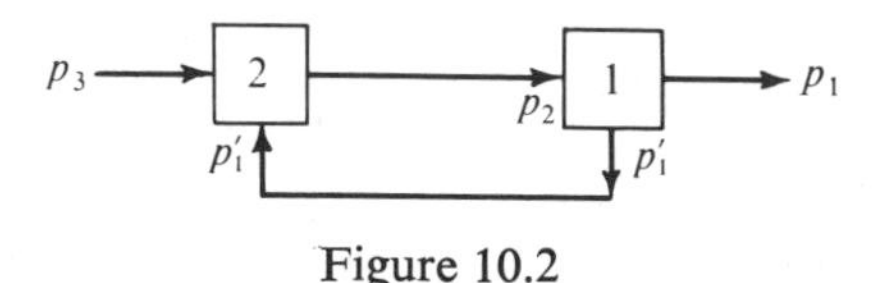

Figure 10.2

we have only to substitute $p_2 = q_1$ in equation (10.2) and rearrange to give

$$2q_2p_3 - q_2^2 - q_1(1 + 2\lambda q_2) = 0 \tag{10.5}$$

which is clearly incompatible with equation (10.4), unless $\lambda = 0$, that is, there is no feedback.

Now it might be felt that the principle of optimality does guard against this misapplication by its very statement. It will be recalled (p. 27) that it refers to "the state resulting from the first decision" and here p_2 cannot be so described since it results from both the first and second decisions. However, a feedback of state is generally no better than a decision feedback, for if $\mathscr{T}_2$ is a function of p_1 it is thereby also a function of q_1.

As a further example consider a two-stage process where stage 1 has two outputs, one of which influences stage 2. The system is shown in Figure 10.2 and is governed by the transformations:

$$p_2 = \mathscr{T}_2(p_3, p_1'; q_2), \tag{10.6}$$

$$p_1 = \mathscr{T}_1(p_2; q_1), \tag{10.7}$$

$$p_1' = \mathscr{T}_1'(p_2; q_1), \tag{10.8}$$

and again p_1 is to be maximized.

Now

$$\frac{\partial p_1}{\partial q_1} = \frac{\partial \mathscr{T}_1}{\partial p_2}\frac{\partial p_2}{\partial q_1} + \frac{\partial \mathscr{T}_1}{\partial q_1}, \tag{10.9}$$

and setting this equal to zero is not generally the same as applying the principle of optimality in the form that, for given p_2, q_1 must be chosen to maximize p_1, for this would require that $\partial \mathscr{T}_1/\partial q_1$ be zero. It is not the same because the first term does not generally vanish. To evaluate this first term we differentiate equations (10.6) and (10.8) with respect to q_1 keeping q_2 and p_3 constant. Then

$$\frac{\partial p_2}{\partial q_1} = \frac{\partial \mathscr{T}_2}{\partial p_1'}\frac{\partial p_1'}{\partial q_1} = \frac{\partial \mathscr{T}_2}{\partial p_1'}\left(\frac{\partial \mathscr{T}_1'}{\partial p_2}\frac{\partial p_2}{\partial q_1} + \frac{\partial \mathscr{T}_1'}{\partial q_1}\right)$$

or

$$\frac{\partial p_2}{\partial q_1} = \frac{\partial \mathscr{T}_2}{\partial p_1'}\frac{\partial \mathscr{T}_1'}{\partial q_1}\bigg/\left\{1 - \frac{\partial \mathscr{T}_2}{\partial p_1'}\frac{\partial \mathscr{T}_1'}{\partial p_2}\right\}$$

and substituting in (10.9) we have

$$\frac{\partial p_1}{\partial q_1} = \left[\frac{\partial \mathscr{T}_1}{\partial q_1} + \frac{\partial \mathscr{T}_2}{\partial p_1'}\frac{\partial(\mathscr{T}_1, \mathscr{T}_1')}{\partial(p_2, q_1)}\right]\bigg/\left[1 - \frac{\partial \mathscr{T}_2}{\partial p_1'}\frac{\partial \mathscr{T}_1'}{\partial p_2}\right]. \tag{10.10}$$

Assuming that the denominator is not zero the vanishing of $\partial p_1/\partial q_1$ implies the vanishing of $\partial \mathscr{T}_1/\partial q_1$ only if either

$$\frac{\partial(\mathscr{T}_1, \mathscr{T}_1')}{\partial(p_2, q_1)} = 0 \tag{10.11}$$

or

$$\frac{\partial \mathscr{T}_2}{\partial p_1'}\frac{\partial \mathscr{T}_1}{\partial p_2}\frac{\partial \mathscr{T}_1'}{\partial q_1} = 0.$$

The second possibility is trivial since it implies that there either is no effective feedback ($\partial \mathscr{T}_2/\partial p_1' = 0$ or $\partial \mathscr{T}_1'/\partial q_1 = 0$) or that the first stage is stationary ($\partial \mathscr{T}_1/\partial p_2 = 0$). Equation (10.11) is more interesting, however, for it can be nontrivially satisfied if $\mathscr{T}_1'$ is functionally dependent on $\mathscr{T}_1$; $\mathscr{T}_1' = \Phi(\mathscr{T}_1)$.

Lest it be thought that this gives an infallible case let us consider the following example due to Jackson. Let

$$p_2 = \tfrac{1}{4}p_3 + \tfrac{3}{4}p_1', \tag{10.12}$$

$$p_1 = p_1' = 2p_2 - q_1^2. \tag{10.13}$$

Then

$$\frac{\partial \mathscr{T}_1}{\partial q_1} = -2q_1, \qquad \frac{\partial^2 \mathscr{T}_1}{\partial q_1^2} = -2$$

so that $q_1 = 0$ gives a maximum of p_1 with constant p_2. In fact this maximum is $p_1 = 2p_2$ and so substituting in the first equation

$$p_2 = \tfrac{1}{4}p_3 + \tfrac{3}{2}p_2$$

or

$$p_2 = -\tfrac{1}{2}p_3,$$

and so

$$p_{1\,\max} = -p_3.$$

But substituting from (10.12) into (10.13) we have

$$p_1 = -p_3 + 2q_1^2,$$

and here evidently $q_1 = 0$ is a minimum and not a maximum.

A slightly more general example (also due to Jackson) shows the nature of the difficulty even more clearly. Let

$$p_2 = (1 - \lambda)p_3 + \lambda p_1' \tag{10.14}$$

$$p_1 = p_1' = \mathscr{T}_1(p_2, q_1) \tag{10.15}$$

and the objective again be the maximization of p_1. Suppose that $\mathscr{T}_1$ has a single maximum with respect to q_1 when p_2 is held constant; this occurs when $q_1 = q_1^*(p_2)$, the value of q_1 for which $\partial \mathscr{T}_1/\partial q_1 = 0$ and $\partial^2 \mathscr{T}_1/\partial q_1^2 < 0$. Now by equation (10.10)

$$\frac{\partial p_1}{\partial q_1} = \frac{\partial \mathscr{T}_1}{\partial q_1} \bigg/ \left\{1 - \lambda \frac{\partial \mathscr{T}_1}{\partial p_2}\right\}$$

and this is zero for $q_1 = q_1^*(p_2)$. However,

$$\frac{\partial^2 p_1}{\partial q_1^2} = \frac{\partial^2 \mathscr{T}_1}{\partial q_1^2} \bigg/ \left\{1 - \lambda \frac{\partial \mathscr{T}_1}{\partial p_2}\right\} + \lambda \frac{\partial \mathscr{T}_1}{\partial q_1} \frac{\partial^2 \mathscr{T}_1}{\partial p_2 \, \partial q_1} \bigg/ \left\{1 - \lambda \frac{\partial \mathscr{T}_1}{\partial p_2}\right\}^2$$

and at the extremum the second term is zero. Thus although $\partial p_1/\partial q_1 = 0$, $\partial^2 p_1/\partial q_1^2$ will become positive if $\lambda \partial \mathscr{T}_1/\partial p_2$ is greater than one, and the maximum of p_1 for constant p_2 will become a minimum if p_3 is really the variable being held constant. Thus so long as $\lambda < 1/(\partial \mathscr{T}_1/\partial p_2)$ the principle of optimality in its immediate form can be applied, which is the same as saying that there is a limit to the amount of feedback that can be tolerated.

There is indeed an interesting physical interpretation to this need for a weak feedback. For we may say that $\partial \mathscr{T}_2/\partial p_1' =$ effect on p_2 of a small change in p_1', and $\partial \mathscr{T}_1'/\partial p_2 =$ effect on p_1' of a small change in p_2. Their product is the effect on p_1' (or p_2) of a small change in itself after this change has acted on p_2 (or p_1'). If this is greater than 1 the feedback process is unstable and this inversion of the nature of the extremum is one of the unfortunate results.

Suppose however that we have a more general objective function and wish to maximize

$$\mathscr{O} = P(p_1, q_1, q_2) \tag{10.16}$$

with equations (10.6), (10.7), and (10.8) governing the process. If, whatever p_3 and q_2 may be, stage 1 should use the q_1 that maximizes P for given p_2 then q_1 would satisfy

$$\frac{\partial P}{\partial p_1} \frac{\partial \mathscr{T}_1}{\partial q_1} + \frac{\partial P}{\partial q_1} = 0. \tag{10.17}$$

But in view of the feedback the true necessary condition is

$$\frac{\partial P}{\partial p_1}\frac{\partial p_1}{\partial q_1} + \frac{\partial P}{\partial q_1} = 0, \tag{10.18}$$

where $\partial p_1/\partial q_1$ is given by (10.10). The only way in which equations (10.17) and (10.18) can be the same is the trivial case in which feedback is really eliminated, that is, $\partial \mathscr{T}_2/\partial p_1' = 0$, and not even the functional dependence of $\mathscr{T}_1$ on $\mathscr{T}_1'$ is sufficient.

To summarize:

(i) There are some special cases which admit of the principle of optimality when the feedback is sufficiently weak.

(ii) Even in these cases the increase of feedback may cause an extremum found by dynamic programming to be the opposite of what was intended.

(iii) The slightest sophistication of the objective function, or increase in dimensionality, is apt to destroy the applicability of the principle even for weak feedback.

It appears therefore that when an extension is made to any system other than the straight chain of stages a very careful examination is necessary. The safeguard against these rash extensions is actually contained in Bellman's formulation of the principle of optimality if a strict interpretation is put on the words "the state resulting from the first decision." With this in mind let us examine a few of the extensions that may be made—usually at the expense of enlarging the state vector.

10.2. Some extensions

(i) *Straight feed-forward.* Consider the system shown in Figure 10.3 in

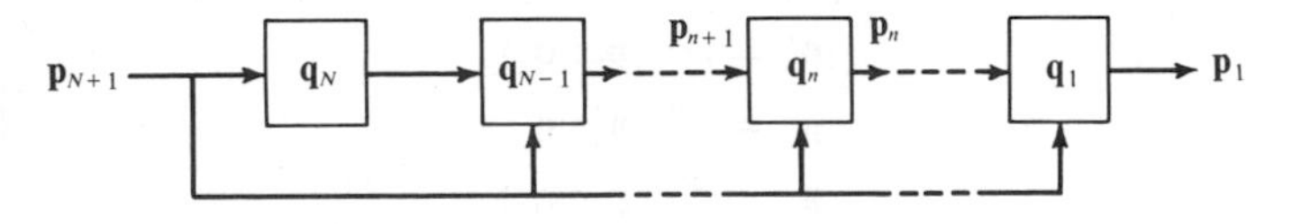

Figure 10.3

which the state of the primary feed affects not only stage N but also the succeeding stages. The transformation by stage n may be written

$$\mathbf{p}_n = \mathscr{T}_n(\mathbf{p}_{n+1}, \mathbf{p}_{N+1}; \mathbf{q}_n) \tag{10.19}$$

and one of the components of the decision $\mathbf{q}_n$ is the extent to which $\mathbf{p}_{N+1}$ should affect the transformation of the state $\mathbf{p}_{n+1}$ to $\mathbf{p}_n$. If

$$\mathscr{O} = \sum_1^N P_n(\mathbf{p}_{n+1}, \mathbf{p}_{N+1}; \mathbf{q}_n) \tag{10.20}$$

the dynamic programming algorithm is immediately applicable if we set

$$f_n(\mathbf{p}_{n+1}; \mathbf{p}_{N+1}) = \operatorname*{Max}_{\mathbf{q}_n, \dots, \mathbf{q}_1} \left[\sum_1^n P_r \right] \tag{10.21}$$

$$= \operatorname*{Max}_{\mathbf{q}_n} [P_n + f_{n-1}(\mathbf{p}_n; \mathbf{p}_{N+1})]. \tag{10.22}$$

Then for the whole process

$$f_N(\mathbf{p}_{N+1}) = f_N(\mathbf{p}_{N+1}; \mathbf{p}_{N+1}). \tag{10.23}$$

Here it is perhaps necessary to enlarge the state vector by writing $f_n(\mathbf{p}_{n+1}; \mathbf{p}_{N+1})$. In many cases, however, $\mathbf{p}_{N+1}$ can be regarded as a fixed set of parameters or can be taken as the origin in state space, in which case there is really no greater problem of dimensionality than before.

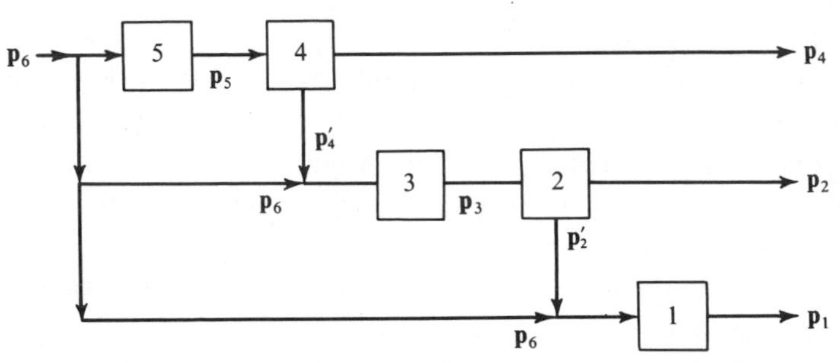

Figure 10.4

(ii) *Cascaded feed-forward.* Roberts has considered a process of the type shown in Figure 10.4 for five stages. The transformations are:

$$\begin{aligned}
\mathbf{p}_1 &= \mathscr{T}_1(\mathbf{p}_2', \mathbf{p}_6; \mathbf{q}_1) \\
\mathbf{p}_2 &= \mathscr{T}_2(\mathbf{p}_3; \mathbf{q}_2) \\
\mathbf{p}_2' &= \mathscr{T}_2'(\mathbf{p}_3; \mathbf{q}_2) \\
\mathbf{p}_3 &= \mathscr{T}_3(\mathbf{p}_4'; \mathbf{p}_6; \mathbf{q}_3) \\
\mathbf{p}_4 &= \mathscr{T}_4(\mathbf{p}_5; \mathbf{q}_4) \\
\mathbf{p}_4' &= \mathscr{T}_4'(\mathbf{p}_5; \mathbf{q}_4) \\
\mathbf{p}_5 &= \mathscr{T}_5(\mathbf{p}_6; \mathbf{q}_5).
\end{aligned} \tag{10.24}$$

Then the optimization can be performed stage by stage as follows:

$$\begin{aligned}
f_1(\mathbf{p}_2', \mathbf{p}_6) &= \operatorname*{Max}_{\mathbf{q}_1} \{P_1(\mathbf{p}_2', \mathbf{p}_6; \mathbf{q}_1)\} \\
f_2(\mathbf{p}_3, \mathbf{p}_6) &= \operatorname*{Max}_{\mathbf{q}_2} \{P_2(\mathbf{p}_3; \mathbf{q}_2) + f_1(\mathbf{p}_2', \mathbf{p}_6)\}
\end{aligned} \tag{10.25}$$

and so on to

$$f_5(\mathbf{p}_6) = \operatorname*{Max}_{\mathbf{q}_5} \{P_5(\mathbf{p}_6; \mathbf{q}_6) + f_4(\mathbf{p}_5, \mathbf{p}_6)\}.$$

Again the increase in dimensionality may not be as serious as it looks at first.

(iii) *Branching processes.* Mitten and Nemhauser have considered branching processes of the type in Figure 10.5. With a notation that should be fairly obvious the two branches can be treated separately to give $f_{N'}(\mathbf{p}_{(N+1)'})$ and

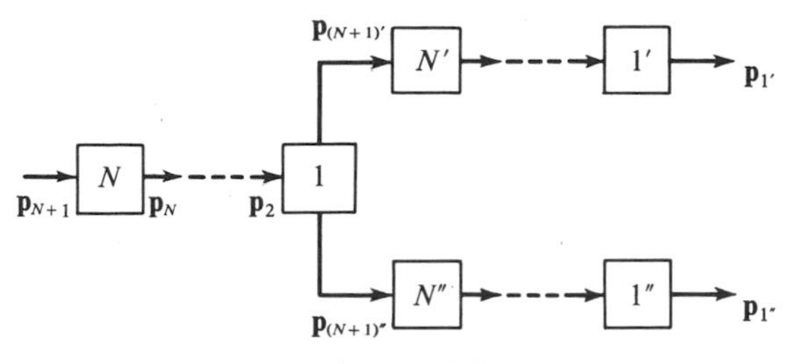

Figure 10.5

$f_{N''}(\mathbf{p}_{(N+1)''})$, the maximum returns from the separate branches. Stage 1 produces two products, whose states are given by

$$\mathbf{p}_{(N+1)'} = \mathscr{T}_1'(\mathbf{p}_2; \mathbf{q}_1), \; \mathbf{p}_{(N+1)''} = \mathscr{T}_1''(\mathbf{p}_2; \mathbf{q}_1). \tag{10.26}$$

Then

$$f_1(\mathbf{p}_2) = \operatorname*{Max}_{\mathbf{q}_1} [P_1(\mathbf{p}_2; \mathbf{q}_1) + f_{N'}(\mathbf{p}_{(N+1)'}) + f_{N''}(\mathbf{p}_{(N+1)''})] \tag{10.27}$$

and

$$f_n(\mathbf{p}_{n+1}) = \operatorname*{Max}_{\mathbf{q}_n} [P_n(\mathbf{p}_{n+1}; \mathbf{q}_n) + f_{n-1}(\mathbf{p}_n)], \qquad n = 2, \cdots, N. \tag{10.28}$$

(iv) *Feedforward loop.* Mitten and Nemhauser have also considered the case in which the branch comes together again to form as in Figure 10.6.

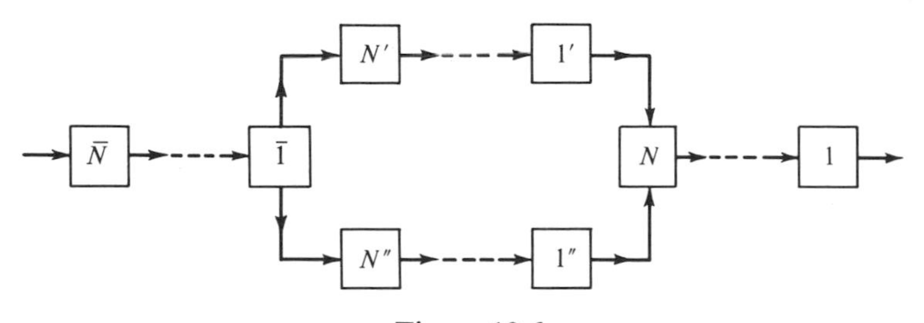

Figure 10.6

Here we can start optimizing the final straight chain in a perfectly direct fashion:

$$f_n(\mathbf{p}_{n+1}) = \operatorname*{Max}_{\mathbf{q}_n} [P_n(\mathbf{p}_{n+1}; \mathbf{q}_n) + f_{N-1}(\mathbf{p}_n)], \qquad n = 1, \cdots, N-1. \tag{10.29}$$

But for stage N the two distinct feeds must be taken into account

$$f_N(\mathbf{p}_{1'}, \mathbf{p}_{1''}) = \operatorname*{Max}_{\mathbf{q}_N} [P_N(\mathbf{p}_{1'}, \mathbf{p}_{1''}; \mathbf{q}_N) + f_{N-1}(\mathbf{p}_N)]. \tag{10.30}$$

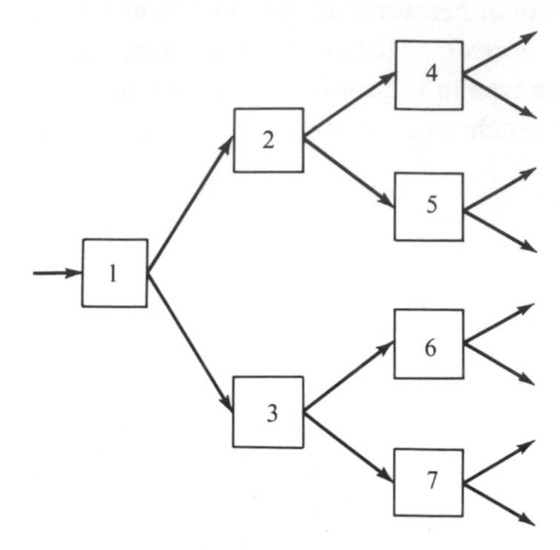

Figure 10.7

Now keeping $\mathbf{p}_{1''}$ as a parameter, we can work back along the upper branch and

$$f_{n'}(\mathbf{p}_{(n+1)'}, \mathbf{p}_{1''}) = \operatorname*{Max}_{\mathbf{q}_{n'}} [P_{n'}(\mathbf{p}_{(n+1)'}; \mathbf{q}_{n'}) + f_{(n-1)'}(\mathbf{p}_{n'}, \mathbf{p}_{1''})], \qquad n' = 1', \cdots, N', \tag{10.31}$$

with

$$f_{0'}(\mathbf{p}_{1'}, \mathbf{p}_{1''}) = f_N(\mathbf{p}_{1'}, \mathbf{p}_{1''}). \tag{10.32}$$

Again keeping $\mathbf{p}_{(N+1)'}$ as a parameter we may work the lower branch

$$f_{n''}(\mathbf{p}_{(N+1)'}, \mathbf{p}_{(n+1)''}) = \operatorname*{Max}_{\mathbf{q}_{n''}} [P_{n''}(\mathbf{p}_{(n+1)''}; \mathbf{q}_{n'}) + f_{(n-1)''}(\mathbf{p}_{(N+1)'}, \mathbf{p}_{n''})], \qquad n'' = 1'', \cdots, N'', \tag{10.33}$$

with

$$f_{0''}(\mathbf{p}_{(N+1)'}, \mathbf{p}_{1''}) = f_{N'}(\mathbf{p}_{(N+1)'}, \mathbf{p}_{1''}). \tag{10.34}$$

For the junction state 1

$$f_{\bar{1}}(\mathbf{p}_{\bar{2}}) = \operatorname*{Max}_{\mathbf{q}_{\bar{1}}} [P_{\bar{1}}(\mathbf{p}_{\bar{2}}, \mathbf{q}_{\bar{1}}) + f_{N'}(\mathbf{p}_{(N+1)'}, \mathbf{p}_{(N+1)''})] \tag{10.35}$$

and thereafter

$$f_{\bar{n}}(p_{\overline{n+1}}) = \operatorname*{Max}_{\mathbf{q}_{\bar{n}}} [P_{\bar{n}}(\mathbf{p}_{\overline{n+1}}, \mathbf{q}_{\bar{n}}) + f_{\overline{n-1}}(\mathbf{p}_{\bar{n}})], \qquad n = 2, \cdots, N. \tag{10.36}$$

(v) *Exponential cascade.* An exponential cascade in which each unit produces ρ distinct product streams has $\rho^{\sigma-1}$ units in its σth stratum. The case of $\rho = 2$ is illustrated in Figure 10.7; here the first stratum is a single stage whose products feed two units in the second stratum and so on. The essential feature of the exponential cascade is that there is no recombination of streams.

To avoid a cumbersome notation we will illustrate the case shown of $\rho = 2$, $\sigma = 3$. Let the upper product stream going from state n to stage $2n$ be denoted

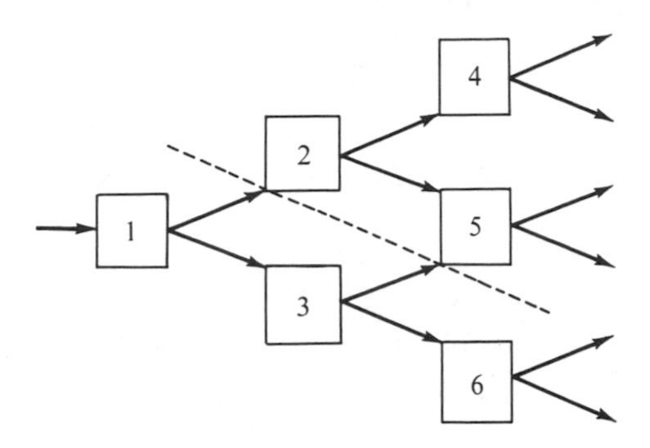

Figure 10.8

by $\mathbf{p}_n'$ and the lower going from n to $(2n + 1)$ by $\mathbf{p}_n''$. If the stages 4–7 are not identical we need first the optimal one-stage profits

$$f_1^{(n)}(\mathbf{p}) = \underset{\mathbf{q}_1}{\text{Max}}\, [P_n(\mathbf{p}, \mathbf{q}_n)], \qquad n = 4, \cdots, 7. \tag{10.37}$$

Then for two strata

$$f_2^{(2)}(\mathbf{p}_1') = \underset{\mathbf{q}_2}{\text{Max}}\, [P_2(\mathbf{p}_1', \mathbf{q}_2) + f_1^{(4)}(\mathbf{p}_2') + f_1^{(5)}(\mathbf{p}_2'')] \tag{10.38}$$

and

$$f_2^{(3)}(\mathbf{p}_1'') = \underset{\mathbf{q}_3}{\text{Max}}\, [P_3(\mathbf{p}_1'', \mathbf{q}_3) + f_1^{(6)}(\mathbf{p}_3') + f^{(7)}(\mathbf{p}_3'')]. \tag{10.39}$$

Finally,

$$f_3(\mathbf{p}_0) = \underset{\mathbf{q}_1}{\text{Max}}\, [P_1(\mathbf{p}_0, \mathbf{q}_1) + f_2^{(2)}(\mathbf{p}_1') + f_2^{(3)}(\mathbf{p}_1'')]. \tag{10.40}$$

(vi) *Triangular cascade.* If the distinctive feature of the exponential cascade, the fact that no two streams come together, is dropped, then dynamic programming may only be applied at the expense of enlarging the state vector. Consider the simplest case of a triangular cascade as shown in Figure 10.8.

Here stage 5 is fed from $\mathbf{p}_2''$ and $\mathbf{p}_3'$ and so the maximum profit from it is a function of both,

$$f_1^{(5)}(\mathbf{p}_2'', \mathbf{p}_3') = \underset{\mathbf{q}_5}{\text{Max}}\, [P_5(\mathbf{p}_2'', \mathbf{p}_3', \mathbf{q}_5)]. \tag{10.41}$$

For stages 4 and 6 we have simpler single-stage optima

$$f_1^{(4)}(\mathbf{p}_2') = \underset{\mathbf{q}_4}{\text{Max}}\, [P_4(\mathbf{p}_2', \mathbf{q}_4)], \qquad f_1^{(6)}(\mathbf{p}_3'') = \underset{\mathbf{q}_6}{\text{Max}}\, [P_6(\mathbf{p}_3'', \mathbf{q}_6)]. \tag{10.42}$$

To obtain a two-stage policy we have to disect as shown by the broken line. If $f_2(\mathbf{p}_1', \mathbf{p}_3')$ is the maximum profit from stages 2, 4, and 5, then

$$f_2^{(2)}(\mathbf{p}_1', \mathbf{p}_3') = \text{Max}\,[P_2(\mathbf{p}_1', \mathbf{q}_2) + f_1^{(4)}(\mathbf{p}_2') + f_1^{(5)}(\mathbf{p}_2'', \mathbf{p}_3')]. \tag{10.43}$$

We may now add stage 3 and obtain

$$f_2^{(3)}(\mathbf{p}_1', \mathbf{p}_1'') = \underset{\mathbf{q}_3}{\text{Max}}\,[P_3(\mathbf{p}_1'', \mathbf{q}_3) + f_2^{(2)}(\mathbf{p}_1', \mathbf{p}_3') + f_1^{(6)}(\mathbf{p}_3'')]. \tag{10.44}$$

Then, finally,

$$f_3(\mathbf{p}_0) = \underset{\mathbf{q}_1}{\text{Max}}\,[P_1(\mathbf{p}_0, \mathbf{q}_1) + f_2^{(3)}(\mathbf{p}_1', \mathbf{p}_1'')]. \tag{10.45}$$

We see that in this case the optimization has been performed at the price of doubling the number of state variables. A triangular cascade with σ strata will generally require a $(\sigma - 1)$-fold increase in the number of state variables.

10.3. The feedback loop, I. (Reversal of direction)

It should now be clear that the attempt to extend the application of dynamic programming must face the difficulties of increased dimensionality. If the inevitable is accepted we can still make some progress in cases where the dimensionality is not too great, particularly if care is taken to see that it does not increase unnecessarily. The whole subject has yet to be put into its final order and shape, but some indication of the progress that has been made can be given. In this section we will treat the feedback loop by the method of Mitten and Nemhauser. In the next section, Wilde's method of absorbing branches will be used. For the feedback loop these methods are superior to the use of our own "platitudinous" principle of optimality, which however does find application to the optimization of the countercurrent system.

The core of Mitten and Nemhauser's method is the fact that the direction of optimization may be reversed. It is clear that in many cases the transformation effected by the stage may be inverted and instead of the equation

$$\mathbf{p}_n = \mathscr{T}_n(\mathbf{p}_{n+1}, \mathbf{q}_n) \tag{10.46}$$

determining the output state in terms of the input and decision, we have an equation

$$\mathbf{p}_{n+1} = \bar{\mathscr{T}}_n(\mathbf{p}_n, \mathbf{q}_n) \tag{10.47}$$

that answers the question, "what is the input for which stage n gives output $\mathbf{p}_n$ when the decision variables are $\mathbf{q}_n$?" However, we have insisted that it is of the essence that the optimization of a straight chain should be in the opposite direction to the flow; that is, we obtain first $f_1(\mathbf{p}_2)$, then $f_2(\mathbf{p}_3)$, and so on (see

Figure 2.3). Let us remember that $f_N(\mathbf{p}_{N+1})$ means the maximum value of the objective function $\Sigma_1^N P_n(\mathbf{p}_{n+1}; \mathbf{q}_n)$ when the feed state is $\mathbf{p}_{N+1}$—thus the feed state is given and the final state $\mathbf{p}_1$ is free to find its optimal level. We could, however, pose the problem in the opposite sense by supposing that the feed was not fixed, but free to find its optimal level, whereas the product state $\mathbf{p}_1$ had to assume a given value. Let us write the first function, $f_N(\mathbf{p}_{N+1} \mid \mathbf{p}_1)$, the state variables after the bar being free and those before it being prescribed. The optimum when $\mathbf{p}_1$ is prescribed and $\mathbf{p}_{N+1}$ left free is thus $f_N(\mathbf{p}_1 \mid \mathbf{p}_{N+1})$. Let us recall too that we have been interested in problems where both $\mathbf{p}_1$ and $\mathbf{p}_{N+1}$ are prescribed (as in section 2.4, problem Ia); these might be written $f_N(\mathbf{p}_1, \mathbf{p}_{N+1} \mid\,)$. On the other hand, having found $f_N(\mathbf{p}_{N+1} \mid \mathbf{p}_1)$ we might have asked what the most profitable $\mathbf{p}_{N+1}$ should be and have obtained $f_N(\,\mid \mathbf{p}_1, \mathbf{p}_{N+1})$. These various optima are related as follows:

$$f_N(\mathbf{p}_{N+1} \mid \mathbf{p}_1) = \operatorname*{Max}_{\mathbf{p}_1} f_N(\mathbf{p}_1, \mathbf{p}_{N+1} \mid\,), \tag{10.48}$$

$$f_N(\mathbf{p}_1 \mid \mathbf{p}_{N+1}) = \operatorname*{Max}_{\mathbf{p}_{N+1}} f_N(\mathbf{p}_1, \mathbf{p}_{N+1} \mid\,), \tag{10.49}$$

$$f_N(\,\mid \mathbf{p}_1, \mathbf{p}_{N+1}) = \operatorname*{Max}_{\mathbf{p}_1} f_N(\mathbf{p}_1 \mid \mathbf{p}_{N+1}) = \operatorname*{Max}_{\mathbf{p}_{N+1}} f_N(\mathbf{p}_{N+1} \mid \mathbf{p}_1). \tag{10.50}$$

The optimum with $\mathbf{p}_1$ prescribed and $\mathbf{p}_{N+1}$ free is not as odd as it might at first seem. Moreover it can be obtained by working from stage N up to stage 1. The return from a single stage (in this case stage N) when its output is given is $f_1(\mathbf{p}_N \mid \mathbf{p}_{N+1})$. Using the inverted transformation we may write the profit $P_N(\mathbf{p}_{N+1}, \mathbf{p}_N, \mathbf{q}_N)$ as

$$\bar{P}_N(\mathbf{p}_N, \mathbf{q}_N) = P_N(\bar{\mathscr{T}}_N(\mathbf{p}_N; \mathbf{q}_N), \mathbf{p}_N, \mathbf{q}_N). \tag{10.51}$$

Thus

$$f_1(\mathbf{p}_N \mid \mathbf{p}_{N+1}) = \operatorname*{Max}_{\mathbf{q}_N} \bar{P}_N(\mathbf{p}_N, \mathbf{q}_N). \tag{10.52}$$

But the principle of optimality itself may be inverted in considering optimal policies for operation with respect to a given final state by saying that whatever the final state and decision may be, the preceding decisions must constitute an optimal policy with respect to the state resulting from them. For stages N and $N - 1$ we have

$$f_2(\mathbf{p}_{N-1} \mid \mathbf{p}_{N+1}) = \operatorname*{Max}_{\mathbf{q}_{N-1}} [\bar{P}_{N-1}(\mathbf{p}_{N-1}, \mathbf{q}_{N-1}) + f_1(\mathbf{p}_N \mid \mathbf{p}_{N+1})], \tag{10.53}$$

and in general

$$f_{r+1}(\mathbf{p}_{N-r} \mid \mathbf{p}_{N+1}) = \operatorname*{Max}_{\mathbf{q}_{N-r}} [\bar{P}_{N-r}(\mathbf{p}_{N-r}, \mathbf{q}_{N-r}) + f_r(\mathbf{p}_{N-r+1} \mid \mathbf{p}_{N+1})],$$

$$r = 0, 1, \cdots, N - 1. \tag{10.54}$$

The more usual problem of finding $f_N(\mathbf{p}_{N+1} \mid \mathbf{p}_1)$ can be solved rather indirectly by first solving for $f_N(\mathbf{p}_1, \mathbf{p}_{N+1} \mid)$ and then using equation (10.48). To do this we recognize that if $\mathbf{p}_{N+1}$ and $\mathbf{p}_N$ are both prescribed then there will be restrictions on the admissible policy for $\mathbf{q}_N$. In fact (as in Problem Ia, section 2.4) $\mathbf{q}_N$ may be completely determined or $\mathbf{p}_N$ and $\mathbf{p}_{N+1}$ might impose some restrictions on each other. We may however write

$$f_1(\mathbf{p}_N, \mathbf{p}_{N+1} \mid) = \operatorname*{Max}_{\mathbf{q}_N} P(\mathbf{p}_N, \mathbf{q}_N) \tag{10.55}$$

remembering that $\mathbf{q}_N$ may not be at our disposal at all so that the maximum is

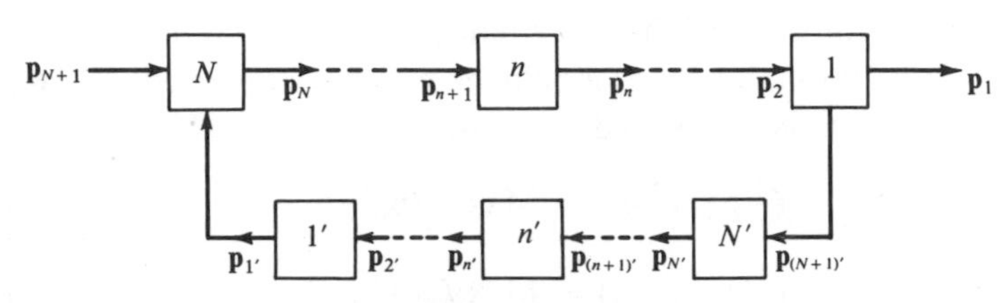

Figure 10.9

a forced one. After this the equation (10.54) applies with the bar in the brackets moved beyond both arguments. This is equivalent to the platitudinous principle considered later, but we need to make the point here that it is possible to optimize in the direction of the stream even when the feed state is given.

Consider now the feedback loop shown in Figure 10.9. None of the stages has more than one input or output except stage N and stage 1. For them the stage transformations read

$$\mathbf{p}_N = \mathscr{T}_N(\mathbf{p}_{N+1}, \mathbf{p}_{1'}; \mathbf{q}_N), \tag{10.56}$$

$$\mathbf{p}_1 = \mathscr{T}_1(\mathbf{p}_2; \mathbf{q}_1), \tag{10.57}$$

$$\mathbf{p}_{(N+1)'} = \mathscr{T}_1'(\mathbf{p}_2; \mathbf{q}_1). \tag{10.58}$$

By Mitten and Nemhauser's method we would first optimize stage 1 with the restriction that $\mathbf{p}_{(N+1)'}$ must be prescribed. Let

$$g_1(\mathbf{p}_2, \mathbf{p}_{(N+1)'}) = \operatorname*{Max}_{\mathbf{q}_1} P_1(\mathbf{p}_2, \mathbf{q}_1) \tag{10.59}$$

subject to

$$\mathscr{T}_1'(\mathbf{p}_2, \mathbf{q}_1) = \mathbf{p}_{(N+1)'}. \tag{10.60}$$

We may then proceed normally down the main branch keeping $\mathbf{p}_{(N+1)'}$ as parameter. Thus

$$g_n(\mathbf{p}_{n+1}, \mathbf{p}_{(N+1)'}) = \operatorname*{Max}_{\mathbf{q}_n} [P_n(\mathbf{p}_{n+1}, \mathbf{q}_n) + g_{n-1}(\mathbf{p}_n, \mathbf{p}_{(N+1)'})] \tag{10.61}$$

for $n = 1, 2, \cdots, N - 1$. Now let us hold $\mathbf{p}_N$ fixed and optimize in the direction of flow down the feedback branch. Let

$$h_1(\mathbf{p}_N, \mathbf{p}_{N'}) = \underset{\mathbf{q}_{N'}}{\text{Max}} [\bar{P}_{N'}(\mathbf{p}_{N'}, \mathbf{q}_{N'}) + g_{N-1}(\mathbf{p}_N, \mathbf{p}_{(N+1)'})] \tag{10.62}$$

where the bar denotes that $P_{N'}$ has been expressed in terms of $\mathbf{p}_{N'}$ by the inverted transformation

$$\mathbf{p}_{(N+1)'} = \bar{\bar{\mathscr{T}}}_{N'}(\mathbf{p}_{N'}, \mathbf{q}_{N'}) \tag{10.63}$$

and this transformation is also used to give the second argument in g_{N-1}. We can now write

$$h_{N'-n'+1}(\mathbf{p}_N, \mathbf{p}_{n'}) = \underset{\mathbf{q}_{n'}}{\text{Max}} [\bar{P}_{n'}(\mathbf{p}_{n'}, \mathbf{q}_{n'}) + h_{N'-n'}(\mathbf{p}_N, \mathbf{p}_{n'+1})] \tag{10.64}$$

for $n' = N' - 1, N' - 2, \cdots, 1'$. We observe that the suffix on h is the number of stages of the feedback branch that have been considered so that $h_{N'}(\mathbf{p}_N, \mathbf{p}_{1'})$ is the maximum profit from all stages except stage N when $\mathbf{p}_N$ and $\mathbf{p}_{1'}$ are prescribed. Stage N may now be brought into the picture by

$$f_{N+N'}(\mathbf{p}_{N+1}) \underset{\mathbf{p}_{1'}\mathbf{q}_N}{\text{Max}} [P_N(\mathbf{p}_{N+1}, \mathbf{p}_{1'}, \mathbf{q}_N) + h_{N'}(\mathbf{p}_N, \mathbf{p}_{1'})] \tag{10.65}$$

where we now recognize that $\mathbf{p}_{1'}$ should not be prescribed but must be allowed to find its optimal level.

It should be clear that the method will apply equally well if there are branches at either or both ends. If $\mathbf{p}_1$ is the feed to a straight chain branch we may add its maximum return which is a function of $\mathbf{p}_1$ to P_1 in equation (10.59). If $\mathbf{p}_{N+1}$ is the product of series of stages we may treat the whole system of stages in Figure 10.9 as an additional stage with return $f_{N+N'}(\mathbf{p}_{N+1})$.

The price paid for the optimization of the feedback loop is the increase in dimensionality involved in carrying $\mathbf{p}_{(N+1)'}$ and $\mathbf{p}_N$ parametrically in the g_n and $h_{n'}$.

10.4. The feedback loop, II. (Absorption of branches)

The core of Wilde's approach to the feedback problem lies in recognizing an essential difference between stage N of Figure 10.9 and all the others, even stage 1. Stage 1, like all the stages except stage N, has only a single independent input state vector. The fact that it has two distinguishable output vectors $\mathbf{p}_1$ and $\mathbf{p}_{(N+1)'}$ is not an essential difference in this context. For even if, as we have supposed at the conclusion of the last section, $\mathbf{p}_1$ was the feed to a straight chain of, say, M stages, these could first be optimized to give the maximum return from them as a function of $\mathbf{p}_1$, say, $F_M(\mathbf{p}_1)$. This branch can now be absorbed into stage 1 by replacing $P_1(\mathbf{p}_2, \mathbf{q}_1)$ by

$$\tilde{P}_1(\mathbf{p}_2, \mathbf{q}_1) = P_1(\mathbf{p}_2, \mathbf{q}_1) + F_M[\mathscr{T}_1(\mathbf{p}_2, \mathbf{q}_1)]. \tag{10.66}$$

Stage N differs from the others in having two distinguishable input vectors $\mathbf{p}_{N+1}$ and $\mathbf{p}_{1'}$. It is less obvious that a branch leading up to $\mathbf{p}_{N+1}$ may be absorbed into stage N but this may be accomplished by optimizing in the same direction as the flow. Thus if there are R stages whose product is $\mathbf{p}_{N+1}$ and the optimal return from them *with respect to* $\mathbf{p}_{N+1}$ is $G_R(\mathbf{p}_{N+1})$, we may consider

$$\tilde{P}_N(\mathbf{p}_{1'}, \mathbf{q}_N) = \underset{\mathbf{p}_{N+1}}{\text{Max}}\, [P_N(\mathbf{p}_{N+1}, \mathbf{p}_{1'}, \mathbf{q}_N) + G_R(\mathbf{p}_{N+1})]. \tag{10.67}$$

This optimization is done with respect to the state variable $\mathbf{p}_{N+1}$ and the value which achieves the maximum is a function of both $\mathbf{p}_{1'}$ and $\mathbf{q}_N$. Here there is a local increase in dimensionality but it results in an apparent profit from the stage which has actually absorbed the branch feeding into it. We now have a system like that in Figure 10.9 save that it has profits $\tilde{P}_1$ and $\tilde{P}_N$ at stages 1 and N; $\mathbf{p}_{N+1}$ and $\mathbf{p}_1$ need not be considered further. If there is no branch leading into stage N but $\mathbf{p}_{N+1}$ is fixed then it must be treated as a constant in P_N and $\mathscr{T}_N$ and the same situation has been obtained.

At first sight a circular loop feeding itself would seem a peculiarly useless structure to have obtained, but in fact it can now be optimized with the same amount of labor as was needed in Nemhauser's method. We break the loop at any point, say between stages $1'$ and N and fix $\mathbf{p}_{1'}$. We may now optimize round the loop through stages $1', \cdots, N', 1, \cdots, N$. The typical equations are as follows:

For stage $1'$

$$f_1(\mathbf{p}_{2'}, \mathbf{p}_{1'}) = \underset{\mathbf{q}_{1'}}{\text{Max}}\, P_{1'}(\mathbf{p}_{2'}, \mathbf{q}_{1'}), \tag{10.68}$$

subject to the restriction

$$\mathscr{T}_{1'}(\mathbf{p}_{2'}, \mathbf{q}_{1'}) = \mathbf{p}_{1'}. \tag{10.69}$$

For stages $2', \cdots, N'$

$$f_{r'}(\mathbf{p}_{(r+1)'}, \mathbf{p}_{1'}) = \underset{\mathbf{q}_{r'}}{\text{Max}}\, [P_{r'}(\mathbf{p}_{(r+1)'}, \mathbf{q}_{r'}) + f_{(r-1)'}(\mathbf{p}_{r'}, \mathbf{p}_{1'})], \tag{10.70}$$

$$r' = 2', 3', \cdots, N'.$$

For stage 1,

$$f_{N'+1}(\mathbf{p}_2, \mathbf{p}_{1'}) = \underset{\mathbf{q}_1}{\text{Max}}\, [P_1(\mathbf{p}_2, \mathbf{q}_1) + f_{N'}(\mathbf{p}_{(N+1)'}, \mathbf{p}_{1'})]. \tag{10.71}$$

For stages $2, \cdots, (N-1)$

$$f_{N'+n}(\mathbf{p}_{n+1}, \mathbf{p}_{1'})\ \underset{\mathbf{q}_n}{\text{Max}}\, [P_n(\mathbf{p}_{n+1}) + f_{N'+n-1}(\mathbf{p}_n, \mathbf{p}_{1'})], \tag{10.72}$$

$$n = 2, 3, \cdots, (N-1).$$

For stage N we identify its feed state with $\mathbf{p}_{1'}$ having absorbed the other branch into P_N and

$$f_{N'+N}(\mathbf{p}_{1'}, \mathbf{p}_{1'}) = \underset{\mathbf{q}_N}{\text{Max}} \, [P_N(\mathbf{p}_{1'}, \mathbf{q}_N) + f_{N'+N-1}(\mathbf{p}_N, \mathbf{p}_{1'})]. \quad (10.73)$$

We now recognize that we had no right to fix $\mathbf{p}_{1'}$ which should be allowed to find its optimal level. Thus the final optimum is

$$\underset{\mathbf{p}_{1'}}{\text{Max}} \, [f_{N+N'}(\mathbf{p}_{1'}, \mathbf{p}_{1'})] \quad (10.74)$$

10.5. The platitudinous principle of optimality

Optimizations with both feed and product state specified (such as we have used above) are the subjects of a principle of optimality. This principle is so obvious that we distinguish it from Bellman's profounder notion by the adjective "platitudinous." It states that any arrangement of stages working between two fixed states must do so optimally. Thus, for the straight chain with our standard notation and the bar introduced in section 10.3,

$$f_1(\mathbf{p}_1, \mathbf{p}_2 \,|\,) = \underset{\mathbf{q}_1}{\text{Max}} \, [P_1(\mathbf{p}_2, \mathbf{q}_1)] \quad (10.75)$$

where

$$\mathscr{T}_1(\mathbf{p}_2, \mathbf{q}_1) = \mathbf{p}_1;$$

we recognize that this restriction has suppressed some of the degrees of freedom in the choice of $\mathbf{q}_1$ even to the point of mutually restricting $\mathbf{p}_2$ and $\mathbf{p}_1$. The platitudinous principle of optimality asserts that

$$\begin{aligned} f_n(\mathbf{p}_1, \mathbf{p}_{n+1} \,|\,) &= \underset{\mathbf{q}_n}{\text{Max}} \, [P_n(\mathbf{p}_{n+1}, \mathbf{q}_n) + f_{n-1}(\mathbf{p}_1, \mathbf{p}_n \,|\,)] \\ &= \underset{\mathbf{q}_1}{\text{Max}} \, [P_1(\mathbf{p}_2, \mathbf{q}_1) + f_{n-1}(\mathbf{p}_2, \mathbf{p}_{n+1} \,|\,)] \end{aligned} \quad (10.76)$$

corresponding to dynamic programming in the normal and reverse directions. But it also asserts that

$$f_n(\mathbf{p}_1, \mathbf{p}_{n+1} \,|\,) = \underset{\mathbf{p}_{r+1}}{\text{Max}} \, [f_r(\mathbf{p}_1, \mathbf{p}_{r+1} \,|\,) + f_{n-r}(p_{r+1}, p_{n+1} \,|\,)], \quad (10.77)$$

that is, that the chain can be cut at any point and the two parts can be separately optimized, providing it is recognized that the internal state $\mathbf{p}_{r+1}$ cannot be fixed but must be allowed to find its own level. It will be seen that this has in essence been used in the optimizing along the branches by Nemhauser's method or in treating the closed loop by Wilde's. The price is the increase in the number of state variables which must be carried along. It could be applied to the feedback loop but, since we already have two methods available for this, we will consider instead the countercurrent process.

10.6. Countercurrent systems

The application of the platitudinous principle to the countercurrent system links in a rather interesting way to Bellman's principle with an enlarged concept of state. The system and notation are shown in Figure 10.10. Since

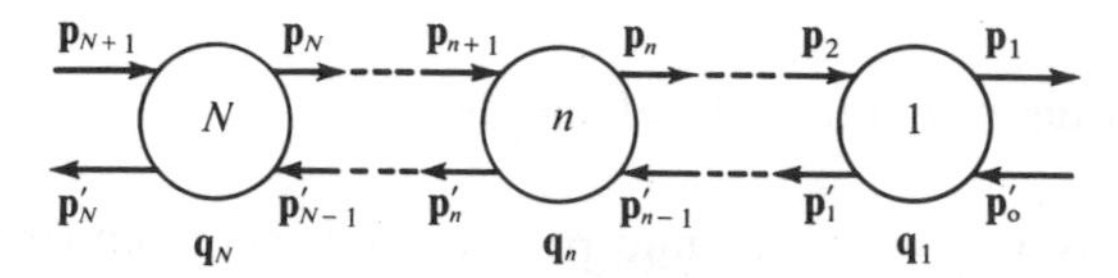

Figure 10.10

streams go in both directions the direction of numbering is arbitrary, but we keep to the convention that the states leaving *n* have suffix *n*; the two streams are distinguished by primed and unprimed state vectors. Normally the equations governing the stage express the outputs in terms of the inputs and the decision

$$\mathbf{p}_n = \mathscr{T}_n(\mathbf{p}_{n+1}, \mathbf{p}'_{n-1}; \mathbf{q}_n), \tag{10.78}$$

$$\mathbf{p}'_n = \mathscr{T}'_n(\mathbf{p}_{n+1}, \mathbf{p}'_{n-1}; \mathbf{q}_n). \tag{10.79}$$

Then the profit from stage *n*, which might be expected to be a function of all four states and the decision, can be similarly expressed as

$$P_n(\mathbf{p}_{n+1}, \mathbf{p}'_{n-1}; \mathbf{q}_n). \tag{10.80}$$

However it is often possible to rearrange the equations and use them to calculate $\mathbf{p}_n$ and $\mathbf{p}'_{n-1}$ in terms of $\mathbf{p}_{n+1}$ and $\mathbf{p}'_n$ by a pair of equations

$$\mathbf{p}_n = \mathscr{R}_n(\mathbf{p}_{n+1}, \mathbf{p}'_n; \mathbf{q}_n) \tag{10.81}$$

$$\mathbf{p}'_{n-1} = \mathscr{R}'_n(\mathbf{p}_{n+1}, \mathbf{p}'_n; \mathbf{q}_n); \tag{10.82}$$

P_n can likewise be expressed in these variables.

Consider stage 1; it works between the states $\mathbf{p}'_0$, $\mathbf{p}_1$, $\mathbf{p}'_1$, $\mathbf{p}_2$. Now in general not all of these state vectors can be arbitrarily specified since some states $\mathbf{p}_1$, $\mathbf{p}'_1$ will not be accessible from $\mathbf{p}'_0$, $\mathbf{p}_2$ with admissible $\mathbf{q}_1$. If any freedom of choice is left to $\mathbf{q}_1$ this must be exercised so as to maximize P_1. Actually the specification of $\mathbf{p}_1$ is not important since it has no effect on the rest of the process, and $\mathbf{p}'_0$ is given for the whole process and may be carried along as a parameter. Thus we may write

$$f_1(\mathbf{p}_2, \mathbf{p}'_1; \mathbf{p}'_0) = \operatorname*{Max}_{\mathbf{q}_1} P_1(\mathbf{p}_2, \mathbf{p}'_1; \mathbf{q}_1) \tag{10.83}$$

subject to the requirement that $\mathbf{p}_0'$ be given by equation (10.82) with $n = 1$. This restriction may not leave any of the decision variables free and may indeed impose limitations on the state variables. If there were only one stage, to which of course the only inputs are $\mathbf{p}_0'$ and $\mathbf{p}_2$, it would now be necessary to choose $\mathbf{p}_1'$ so that f_1 is maximized. Thus for the one-stage process we finally calculate

$$g_1(\mathbf{p}_2, \mathbf{p}_0') = \operatorname*{Max}_{\mathbf{p}_1'} [f_1(\mathbf{p}_2, \mathbf{p}_1'; \mathbf{p}_0')]. \tag{10.84}$$

For a two-stage process we consider the transformation equations in the form of (10.81) and (10.82). If $\mathbf{p}_0'$ is regarded as fixed and a choice of $\mathbf{q}_2$ is made, $\mathbf{p}_2$ and $\mathbf{p}_1'$ can be calculated and stage 1 works between these fixed states. It must therefore do so with maximum profit, thus

$$f_2(\mathbf{p}_3, \mathbf{p}_2'; \mathbf{p}_0') = \operatorname*{Max}_{\mathbf{q}_2} [P_2(\mathbf{p}_3, \mathbf{p}_2'; \mathbf{q}_2) + f_1(\mathbf{p}_2, \mathbf{p}_1'; \mathbf{p}_0')]. \tag{10.85}$$

If there were only two stages, we should finally have to decide on the optimal state $\mathbf{p}_2'$ to obtain

$$g_2(\mathbf{p}_3, \mathbf{p}_0') = \operatorname*{Max}_{\mathbf{p}_2'} [f_2(\mathbf{p}_3, \mathbf{p}_2'; \mathbf{p}_0')]. \tag{10.86}$$

In general

$$f_n(\mathbf{p}_{n+1}, \mathbf{p}_n'; \mathbf{p}_0') = \operatorname*{Max}_{\mathbf{q}_n} [P_n(\mathbf{p}_{n+1}, \mathbf{p}_n'; \mathbf{q}_n) + f_{n-1}(\mathbf{p}_n, \mathbf{p}_{n-1}'; \mathbf{p}_0')] \tag{10.87}$$

and

$$g_n(\mathbf{p}_{n+1}, \mathbf{p}_0') = \operatorname*{Max}_{\mathbf{p}_n'} [f_n(\mathbf{p}_{n+1}, \mathbf{p}_n'; \mathbf{p}_0')], \qquad n = 2, \cdots, N. \tag{10.88}$$

Here the price of optimization in the form of increased dimensionality is clearly seen and any attempt to avoid it by seeking a recursive relation between the g_n is liable to be erroneous. It is also interesting to notice that in equation (10.87) we are using Bellman's principle with an enlarged concept of the notion of the "state resulting from the first decision." For since the equations can be rewritten in the form of equations (10.81) and (10.82) the pair of state vectors $(\mathbf{p}_n, \mathbf{p}_{n-1}')$ can be regarded as the state resulting from the decision $\mathbf{q}_n$ and stage $(\mathbf{p}_{n+1}, \mathbf{p}_n')$. This is consistent with the mathematical formulation of the equations, but not with the physical situation in which it is inputs and not outputs that can be specified. It is for this reason that the specification of $\mathbf{p}_N'$ must finally be relaxed by recognizing that it is not fixed but must have a certain value for the optimality of the whole process, and this value has to be searched out.

Bibliography

10.1. The counterexample given on page 121 is due to

JACKSON, R., "Comments on the Paper 'Optimum Cross-Current Extraction with Product Recycle' by D. F. RUDD and E. D. BLUM," *Chem. Eng. Sci.*, **18** (1963), 215.

10.2. Some examples with feed forward in chemical reactor systems are given in

ARIS, R., *The optimal design of chemical reactors*, New York: Academic Press, Inc., 196

The cascade of Figure 10.4 was given by S. M. Roberts in a paper at the New York meeting of the Am. Inst. Chem. Eng., December, 1961 and at the time of writing has only appeared as preprint 82. His forthcoming book, *Dynamic Programming in Chemical Engineering Process Control* (New York: Academic Press, Inc., 1963), will doubtless contain many examples of interest.

For branching and feed-forward processes (as well as an excellent exposition and clear examples of basic dynamic programming) see

MITTEN, L., and NEMHAUSER, G., "Multistage Optimization," *Chem. Eng. Prog.*, **59** (1963), 52.

10.3. The Treatment of the feedback loop given in this paragraph is that of Mitten and Nemhauser in the above reference. The substance of this and the next section was greatly influenced by correspondence with Wilde and Nemhauser and contains some notions that have not yet appeared elsewhere.

10.6. DRANOFF, J. S., MITTEN, L. G., STEVENS, W. F., and WANNINGER, L. A., "Application of Dynamic Programming to Countercurrent Flow Processes," *Operations Res.*, **9** (1961), 338. This asserts a functional equation between the g_n of section 10.5, and should be corrected in the light of their letter appearing in *Operations Res.*, **10** (1962), 410, which, however, does not achieve the final optimization with respect to the product state.

CHAPTER 11

Some associated mathematical ideas

We shall touch on two mathematical notions which are very close to the heart of the subject. They are, however, somewhat deeper than what has gone before and while it is hoped that they will be clearly presented we shall not try to provide any great wealth of example; this may make the going somewhat heavier for some readers.

11.1. A discrete form of Pontryagin's principle of the maximum

Pontryagin's maximum principle and its application to continuous systems has attracted wide attention. It is equivalent to the principle of optimality and can lead to the same set of equations. Less well known is the discrete version of the principle which has been given independently by Chang and by Katz and which we present here in our standard notation.

We are returning to the basic discrete process of Chapter 2 in which the transformation of state by stage n is

$$\mathbf{p}_n = \mathscr{T}(\mathbf{p}_{n+1}; \mathbf{q}_n) \tag{11.1}$$

or

$$p_{ni} = \mathscr{T}_i(p_{n+1}; q_n), \qquad i = 1, \cdots, s, \tag{11.2}$$

where $\mathbf{p}_n = (p_{n1}, \cdots, p_{ns})$, and the objective is to maximize p_{11}. We will see later how the more general process with $\mathscr{T}$ different at each stage and with an objective function ΣP_n can be reduced to this case by modifying the state vector. The transformations allow us to go forward stage by stage from stage N to stage 1 and so calculate $\mathbf{p}_1$ from $\mathbf{p}_{N+1}$ and $\mathbf{q}_N, \cdots, \mathbf{q}_1$.

Katz introduces a set of adjoint state vectors $\mathbf{z}_n = (z_{n1}, \cdots, z_{ns})$ which are calculable in the reverse direction by a set of equations

$$z_{n+1,j} = \sum_{i=1}^{s} z_{ni} \frac{\partial \mathscr{T}_i(\mathbf{p}_{n+1}; \mathbf{q}_n)}{\partial p_{n+1,j}}. \tag{11.3}$$

Since it is p_{11} that is being maximized, we set

$$z_{11} = 1, \qquad (11.4)$$
$$z_{1j} = 0, \qquad j = 2, \cdots, s.$$

The principle of the maximum then asserts that at each stage $\mathbf{q}_n$ should be chosen (subject, of course, to restrictions of admissibility) so that

$$H_n = \sum_{i=1}^{s} z_{nj}\mathscr{T}_i(\mathbf{p}_{n+1}; \mathbf{q}_n) \qquad (11.5)$$

is maximum.

For the single stage this is obvious, for $\mathbf{p}_2$ is given and $z_{11} = 1$ so that

$$H_1 = \mathscr{T}_1(\mathbf{p}_2; \mathbf{q}_1) \qquad (11.6)$$

and to maximize this is to maximize p_{11} as required. Now the z_{2j} can be calculated from equations (11.3) and

$$z_{2j} = \frac{\partial \mathscr{T}_1(\mathbf{p}_2; \mathbf{q}_1)}{\partial p_{2j}}. \qquad (11.7)$$

But $\mathbf{q}_1$ has been chosen in (11.6) to maximize $\mathscr{T}_1$ so that if we call this maximum

$$f_1(\mathbf{p}_2) = \operatorname*{Max}_{\mathbf{q}_1} [p_{11}] \qquad (11.8)$$

then

$$z_{2j} = \frac{\partial f_1}{\partial p_{2j}}. \qquad (11.9)$$

Again

$$H_2 = \sum_{i=1}^{s} \mathscr{T}_i(\mathbf{p}_3; \mathbf{q}_2)(\partial f_1/\partial p_{2i}), \qquad (11.10)$$

and if we attempt to maximize this with respect to $\mathbf{q}_2$ we shall either satisfy equations such as $\partial H_2/\partial q_{2k} = 0$ or will find a point on the boundary of the region of admissibility at which these derivatives are positive. But

$$\frac{\partial H_2}{\partial q_{2k}} = \sum_{i=1}^{s} \frac{\partial \mathscr{T}_i}{\partial q_{2k}} \frac{\partial f_1}{\partial p_{2i}} = \sum_{i=1}^{s} \frac{\partial p_{2i}}{\partial q_{2k}} \frac{\partial f_1}{\partial p_{2i}} \qquad (11.11)$$

so that we are really seeking

$$\operatorname*{Max}_{\mathbf{q}_2} [f_1(\mathbf{p}_2)], \qquad (11.12)$$

which is just the dynamic programming algorithm. If this maximum is $f_2(\mathbf{p}_3)$, equation (11.3) shows that

$$z_{3j} = \partial f_2/\partial p_{3j}. \qquad (11.13)$$

It follows that the determination of the maximum of H_n at each stage will correspond precisely to the algorithm

$$f_n(\mathbf{p}_{n+1}) = \operatorname*{Max}_{\mathbf{q}_m} [f_{n-1}(\mathbf{p}_n)], \tag{11.14}$$

with which we are familiar.

11.2. Related problems and formulations

The more general problem in which

$$\mathbf{p}_n = \mathscr{T}_n(\mathbf{p}_{n+1}; \mathbf{q}_n) \tag{11.15}$$

and the objective function is

$$\mathcal{O} = \sum_1^N P_n(\mathbf{p}_{n+1}; \mathbf{q}_n) \tag{11.16}$$

can be reduced to the foregoing one by the following changes. Define a new state vector by

$$p'_{n1} = \sum_n^N P_r(\mathbf{p}_{r+1}; \mathbf{q}_r) \tag{11.17}$$

$$p'_{n,i+1} = p_{n,i} \qquad i = 1, \cdots, s \tag{11.18}$$

$$p'_{n,s+2} = n - 1. \tag{11.19}$$

Then we have the transformations

$$p'_{n1} = p'_{n+1,1} + P_n(\mathbf{p}_{n+1}; \mathbf{q}_n) \tag{11.20}$$

$$p'_{n,i+1} = \mathscr{T}_{n,i}(\mathbf{p}_{n+1}; \mathbf{q}_n), \qquad i = 1, \cdots, s \tag{11.21}$$

$$p'_{n,s+2} = p_{n+1,s+2} - 1. \tag{11.22}$$

Then $\mathscr{T}_{n,i}(\mathbf{p}_{n+1}; \mathbf{q}_n)$ can be regarded as $\mathscr{T}_i(\mathbf{p}_{n+1}, n; \mathbf{q}_n) = \mathscr{T}_i(\mathbf{p}'_{n+1}; \mathbf{q}_n)$ and clearly the objective is to maximize p_{11}.

The method is sometimes formulated in what is known as the Hamiltonian style. If, as above, we define the Hamiltonian as

$$H_n = H_n(\mathbf{z}_n, \mathbf{p}_{n+1}; \mathbf{q}_n) = \sum_{i=1}^s z_{ni} \mathscr{T}_i(\mathbf{p}_{n+1}; \mathbf{q}_n) = \mathbf{z}_n \cdot \mathscr{T}(\mathbf{p}_{n+1}, \mathbf{q}_n), \tag{11.23}$$

then the equations can be written

$$p_{ni} = \frac{\partial H_n}{\partial z_{ni}} \qquad \text{or} \qquad \mathbf{p}_n = \nabla_z H_n, \tag{11.24}$$

$$z_{n+1,i} = \frac{\partial H_n}{\partial p_{n+1,i}} \qquad \text{or} \qquad \mathbf{z}_{n+1} = \nabla_p H_n. \tag{11.25}$$

We have $\mathbf{p}_{N+1}$ and $\mathbf{z}_1$ given and $\mathbf{q}_n$ is always chosen to maximize the Hamiltonian.

Our approach has been to relate the method to dynamic programming rather than to present it in the light of its own methods. Katz' proof that this algorithm works is based on a quite different approach.

11.3. Computational considerations

Just as we are forced by dynamic programming to compute more than we need for any one $\mathbf{p}_{N+1}$ (in the form of stored values of $f_n(\mathbf{p}_{n+1})$ for a range of $\mathbf{p}_{n+1}$ from $n = 1$ to $n = N - 1$) so also Pontryagin's method is faced with solving a set of equations with half the conditions at one end and half at the other. If there were only some way of knowing what final state $\mathbf{p}_1$ would correspond to the given $\mathbf{p}_{N+1}$ and optimal policy, it would be possible to use Katz' algorithm and work back from given $\mathbf{p}_1$ and $\mathbf{z}_1$. In general, if we were to do that we would have little hope of hitting a given $\mathbf{p}_{N+1}$ and an undirected trial and error might prove rather wasteful. If a systematic coverage of the whole field is wanted then the dynamic programming algorithm is much the better.

There does, however, seem to be a way in which the trial and error solution of Katz' equations might be directed. It is based on the interpretation of the z_{ni} as $\partial p_1/\partial p_{ni}$ in section 1 of this chapter. Suppose that we are solving the more general problem (section 2) and have an idea what final state $(p'_{12}, \cdots, p'_{1,s+1}) = (p_{11}, \cdots, p_{1s})$ will correspond to the initial state $\mathbf{p}_{N+1}$ we have to match. The adjoint variables of the main problem will of course satisfy the final conditions $z'_{11} = 1$, $z'_{1i} = 0$, $i = 2, \cdots, s + 2$, and the z'_{ni} will be $\partial f_{n-1}/\partial p_{ni}$. In addition to the main problem we will simultaneously compute further s solutions with adjoint variables $\mathbf{z}_n^{(k)}$, $k = 1, \cdots, s$. The final values, $\mathbf{z}_1^{(k)}$, are given by

$$z_{1,k+1}^{(k)} = 1, \qquad z_{1j}^{(k)} = 0, \qquad j \neq k + 1. \tag{11.26}$$

It is as if we were also wishing to solve the s different problems of maximizing $p_{11}, \cdots, p_{1s}$ in turn. However in all cases $\mathbf{q}_n$ is chosen to maximize the H_n formed with adjoint vector $\mathbf{z}'_n$; that is only the optimal policy we finally want is found. It follows that

$$z_{nj}^{(k)} = \frac{\partial p_{1k}}{\partial p_{nj}}, \tag{11.27}$$

where the p_1 is related to p_n through the transformation equations using the optimal policy we desire. Thus

$$z_{N+1,j}^{(k)} = \frac{\partial p_{1k}}{\partial p_{N+1,j}} \tag{11.28}$$

is an element in the Jacobian matrix of final states with respect to initial ones. If our guessed starting values $\bar{\mathbf{p}}_1$ have yielded $\bar{\mathbf{p}}_{N+1}$ different from the desired $\mathbf{p}_{N+1}$ then a better guess at the starting values should be

$$p_{1k} = \bar{p}_{1k} + \sum_{j=1}^{s} (p_{N+1,j} - \bar{p}_{N+1,j}) z_{N+1,j}^{(k)}. \tag{11.29}$$

Where a specific problem has to be solved this method has proved useful in beating the dimensionality rap.

11.4. The maximum transform

A very fascinating new tool for optimization problems has recently been forged by Bellman and Karush. Here we can do little more than introduce the

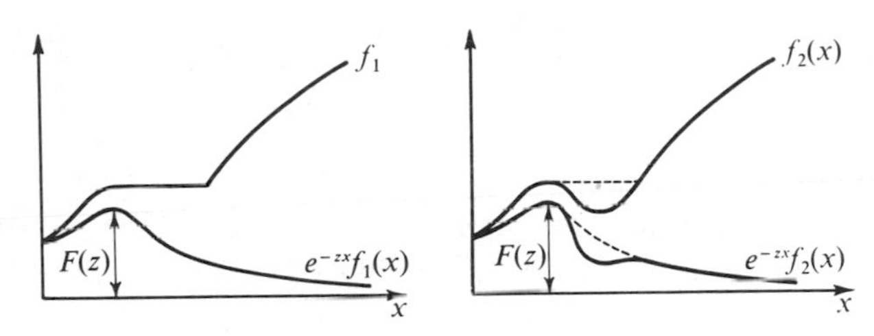

Figure 11.1

reader to it, for its full power and elegance have yet to be exhibited. Just as it is possible to transform a differential equation into an algebraic one by a Fourier transform, so is it possible to transform certain functional equations with a maximand into algebraic equations. The algebraic equation is much easier to solve than the differential and when solved the solution of the original problem is regained by inversion.

For any function $f(x)$, $x \geqslant 0$, we define an associated function

$$F(z) = \operatorname*{Max}_{x \geqslant 0} [e^{-xz} f(x)]. \tag{11.30}$$

Naturally this transform only exists for a certain class of functions, but we can readily see that provided $f(x)$ is continuous and ultimately bounded by some power of x (that is, $f(x)/x^c$ remains finite for some c and $x \to \infty$) the maximum will be defined. The image $f(x)$ of a given transform $F(z)$ may not be unique. For example, in Figure 11.1 two functions $f(x)$ are shown together with a typical product $e^{-xz}f(x)$. Clearly the maximum of $e^{-xz}f(x)$ can only occur at a point where $f'(x)$ is positive and hence these two functions, which differ only in the part of $f_2(x)$ that decreases, lead to the same transform $F(z)$. Because of this we may limit ourselves to a monotone nondecreasing function $f(x)$. To take a particular case, if

$$f(x) = ax^b \tag{1y.31}$$

then

$$F(z) = \max_{x \geqslant 0} [e^{-xz} ax^b] = ae^{-b}(b/z)^b. \tag{11.32}$$

The inversion of the transformation for a function $f(x)$ which is differentiable almost everywhere as well as positive, continuous, and nondecreasing is given by

$$f(x) = \min_{z \geqslant 0} [e^{xz} F(z)]. \tag{11.33}$$

For equation (11.30) means that

$$F(z) > e^{-xz} f(x)$$

except at one point $x = x^0(z)$ where $F(z) = e^{-xz} f(x)$. But if $F(z) > e^{-xz} f(x)$, it follows that $f(x) < e^{xz} F(z)$. Again the inequality will be strict except at $z = z^0(x)$ where z^0 is the inverse function of x^0; this inverse will exist if $(ff' - f'^2)$ does not change sign. But this implies the inversion formula (11.33). The full conditions for the inversion and the precise definition of the class of functions to which the maximum transform is applicable await further investigation.

11.5. The convolution property

An important property of the maximum transform concerns the following problem. If we are given two positive nondecreasing functions $f(x)$ and $g(x)$ and define a third by the equation

$$h(x) = \max_{0 \leqslant y \leqslant x} [f(y)g(x-y)], \tag{11.34}$$

what is the relation between the maximum transforms of these functions?

By definition

$$H(z) = \max_{x \geqslant 0} [e^{-xz} h(x)]$$

$$= \max_{x \geqslant 0} \left\{ e^{-xz} \left[\max_{0 \leqslant y \leqslant x} f(y)g(x-y) \right] \right\}. \tag{11.35}$$

This means that for given z we are seeking the maximum of a function $\varphi(x, y) = e^{-xz}f(y)g(x - y)$ in the triangular region shown in Figure 11.2. Now $\varphi(x, y) = [e^{-yz}f(y)][e^{-(x-y)z}g(x - y)]$ and if we change variables from x, y to $w = x - y$ and y this function is $e^{-yz}f(y)e^{-wz}g(w)$. The region in which we are seeking the maximum is now $y \geqslant 0$, $w \geqslant 0$ and so we can write

$$H(z) = \operatorname*{Max}_{y\geqslant 0} \operatorname*{Max}_{w\geqslant 0} [e^{-yz}f(y)e^{-wz}g(w)]$$

$$= F(z)G(z). \tag{11.36}$$

An extension of this convolution can be made to the product of several

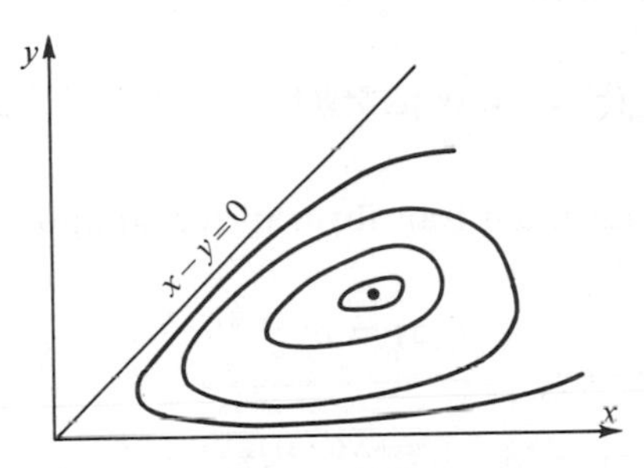

Figure 11.2

functions. If $f(x)$ and $f_i(x_i)$, $i = 1, \cdots, N$ are all suitable functions, whose transforms may be denoted by a capital letter, and

$$x = x_1 + \cdots + x_N, \tag{11.37}$$

then

$$f(x) = \operatorname{Max} [f_1(x_1)f_2(x_2) \cdots f_N(x_N)] \tag{11.38}$$

implies

$$F(z) = F_1(z)F_2(z) \cdots F_N(z). \tag{11.39}$$

Hence by inversion

$$f(x) = \operatorname*{Min}_{z\geqslant 0} [e^{xz}F_1(z) \cdots F_N(z)]. \tag{11.40}$$

11.6. An application of the maximum transform

An elementary application of the maximum transform is afforded by problem Ic of section 2.4. To bring it in line with the notation of the previous paragraph let us define the following variables:

$$x = (k_1 + k_2)\Theta, \qquad x_n = (k_1 + k_2)\theta_n. \tag{11.41}$$

Then the condition that $\Sigma_1^N \theta_n = \Theta$ is the same as equation (11.37). The transformation equation (2.10) for the process can be written

$$\frac{c_e - c_{n+1}}{c_e - c_n} = 1 + x_n. \tag{11.42}$$

If we put

$$f_n(x_n) = 1 + x_n \tag{11.43}$$

then

$$f(x) = \text{Max} \prod_1^N f_n(x_n) = \text{Max} \left[\frac{c_e - c_{N+1}}{c_e - c_1} \right] \tag{11.44}$$

which is what we are seeking.

Now

$$F_n(z) = \underset{x_n \geqslant 0}{\text{Max}} \, [e^{-zx_n}(1 + x_n)] = e^{z-1}/z. \tag{11.45}$$

It follows that the maximum transform of the solution is given by equation (11.39)

$$F(z) = e^{N(z-1)}/z^N \tag{11.46}$$

and the solution itself by

$$f(x) = \underset{z \geqslant 0}{\text{Min}} \, [e^{xz+N(z-1)}/z^N] = \left(1 + \frac{x}{N}\right)^N. \tag{11.47}$$

Thus the greatest extent of conversion that can be achieved with total holding time Θ is

$$c_1 = c_e - (c_e - c_{N+1})\{1 + (k_1 + k_2)\Theta/N\}^{-N}. \tag{11.48}$$

The maximum transform is as yet a relatively unexplored field, but it holds promise of some very elegant and valuable treasure.

Bibliography

11.1. Chang, S. S. L., "Digitized Maximum Principle." *Proc. IRE*, **48** (1960), 2030.

Katz, S., "A Discrete Version of Pontryagin's Maximum Principle." *J. Electron. Control*, **13** (1962), 179.

11.3. Denn, M. M., and Aris, R., "An Iterative Method of Overcoming Difficulties of Dimensionality in Fixed Time Optimization Problems." To appear in *Chem. Eng. Sci.* in 1964.

11.4. Bellman, R., and Karush, W., "On a New Functional Transform in Analysis: The Maximum Transform," *Bull. Amer. Math. Soc.*, **67** (1961), 501.

See also Appendix IV to Bellman, *Applied Dynamic Programming* (Bibliography 1.8) and references given there.

Problems

1. If

$$G(z) = \underset{x \geqslant 0}{\text{Max}} \, [g(x) - xz]$$

show that

$$g(x) = \underset{z \geqslant 0}{\text{Min}} \, [G(z) + xz]$$

and that if

$$h(x) = \underset{x_1 + x_2 = x}{\text{Max}} \, [g_1(x_1) + g_2(x_2)]$$

then

$$H(z) = G_1(z) + G_2(z).$$

This is another form of the maximum transform.

2. If $G(z) = \mathrm{M}[g]$ denotes the transformation of the previous question, show that $M[ag] = aG(z/a)$, $a > 0$.
3. If $h(x)$ is monotonic decreasing let

$$H(z) = \underset{x \geqslant 0}{\text{Min}} \, [h(x) + xz].$$

Find the inversion and convolution properties of this transform.

4. With the information of problem 3 of Chapter 3 solve the dual problem of maximizing the final pressure after N-stage compression with total energy expenditure E.
5. Devise a minimum transform to solve the primal of the above problem.
6. Do the same for problems 4 and 5 of Chapter 3.
7. Show by the use of the maximum transform on problem 6 of Chapter 3 that the minimum potential energy is proportional to $\Sigma_1^N n^2/(n^2 + \mu^2)^{1/2}$ where μ is the root of $\Sigma_1^N \mu/(n^2 + \mu^2)^{1/2} = M$.
8. If

$$\Lambda_N(p) = \underset{b \geqslant 0}{\text{Min}} \, [-L_N(0, b) + bp]$$

and

$$\Lambda_N'(p) = \underset{b \geqslant 0}{\text{Min}} \, [-e^{bc} L_N(0, b) + bp],$$

where L_N is given in problem 3 of Chapter 8, show that

$$L_{2N}(0, b) = \underset{b \geqslant 0}{\text{Max}} \, [bp - \Lambda_N(p) - e^{-bc} \Lambda_N'(pe^{bc})].$$

Index

ARIMIZU, T., 108
ARIS, R., 34, 108, 136, 144
ARROW, K. J., 87
ASH, M., 108

BELLMAN, R., 12, 26, 33, 34, 59, 70, 78, 86, 87, 93, 95, 100, 107, 117, 144
BLUM, E. D., 136
BOLZA, O., 12
Bottleneck problems, 60
BOX, G. E. P., 11
Branching process, 125
BURAS, N., 107

Calculus, differential, 6
Calculus of variations, 10
Cascade
  exponential, 126
  feed-forward, 124
  triangular, 127
Catalyst replacement, 108
CHANG, S. S. L., 137, 144
CHARNES, A., 12
Chemical processes, 108
Communication channel
  erratic, 92
  usefulness of, 92
Communication network, 93
Communication theory, 90
Competitive processes, control of, 80
Constraints
  in continuous processes, 112
  definition of, 18
Continuous problems as limit of discrete, 110
COOPER, W. W., 12
Countercurrent systems, 134
Curve fitting, 97

Decision
  in continuous problems, 112
  definition of, 17
  variables, 17
  vector, 18
Decision process
  discrete, definition of terms in, 17
  without feedback, 27
DENBIGH, K. G., 42
DENN, M. M., 144
DIDO, 1
Difference equation, linear, 73
  general solution of *M*th order, 79
  general solution of second order, 78
Difficult crossing puzzles, 107
Dimensionality, 32
  curse of, 33, 140
  reduction of, in homogeneous equations, 65
  summary of techniques for, 85
  use of solution of difference equation for, 77
Direct calculation, 3, 6
Discrete deterministic decision process, 17
Discrete problems as sampling of continuous, 112
DORFMAN, R., 12
DRANOFF, J. S., 136
DREYFUS, S. E., 12, 59, 86, 87, 95, 107
Duality, 53
Dynamic programming
  economy of, 32
  summary of steps for setting up, 29

Economics, 60
  control in, 72
Expanding grid, menace of, 70
Expenditure
  consumer, 72
  government, 72, 77

Feedback
  absorption of branches, 131
  counterexample for, 119
  reversal of direction, 128

Feed-forward, 123
loop, 125
FEIGEN, M., 107
Forest management, 108
FREIMER, M., 59
FRYER, W. D., 107

Gaussian quadrature, 86
GOLDBERG, S., 87
Government spending, stabilization of economy by, 72
Graphical methods, 37
Growth processes, 108
GRÜTTER, W. F., 108

HALL, W. A., 107
HENDERSON, A., 12
HILTON, H., 107
Homogeneity of equations enabling reduction of dimensionality, 65
HOWARD, R. A., 87

Income, national, 72
Information, negative entropy of, 92
Information theory, 90
Inventory problems, 88
Investment, private, 72
Iterative solution of two point problems, 140

JACKSON, R., 136
Jacobi matrices, 105

KALABA, R., 87, 94, 95, 100, 107, 108
KALMAN, R. E., 117
KARLIN, S., 87
KARUSH, W., 141, 144
KATZ, S., 137, 144
Keynes point, 89
KOTKIN, B., 107

Lag phase, 61
Lagrange multiplier, 54
connection with duality, 58
economic interpretation of, 55
formal application of, 56
LAPIDUS, L., 117
Legendre polynomial, 86
LEITMANN, G., 108
Linearity
difficulties with piecewise, 69, 70
enabling reduction of dimensionality, 65
implying maximum on boundary, 63
persistence of, 63
Linearization, 116

Madison Avenue, 80
MAH, R. H. S., 117
MAHONEY, J. D., 95
Mathematical knowledge assumed, 3
Mathematical modeling, 1
Matrix
differential equations, 116
exponential function of, 117
Jacobi, 105
Maxima, multiple, 6
Maximum transform, 141
application to reactors, 143
convolution of, 142
inversion of, 142
MESSIKOMMER, B. H., 108
MICHAELSON, S., 117
MITTEN, L., 128, 136

NEMHAUSER, G., 128, 136

Objective function
in continuous problems, 112
definition of, 18
Optimality
the boundary between possible and impossible, 53
principle of
formal statement, 27
functional equation, 29
platitudinous, 133
Optimization, a craft, 1

Parameters, 19
Parametric studies, 47
Pest control, 102

Policy
- admissible, 18
- definition of, 18
- nonuniqueness of optimal, 29
- optimal, 19
- second best, 95

Polynomial approximation, 86
Pontryagin's maximum principle, 137
Predation, 104
Principle of the maximum in discrete form, 137
Principle of optimality, see Optimality
Problems, dual, 53
Profit, 19
Programming
- dynamic, 9
- linear, 8
- nonlinear, 9
- relation between linear and dynamic, 58

Reaction
- endothermic, 39
- equilibrium of, 14
- exothermic, 39
- rate of, 13

Reactor
- batch, 113
- holding time of, 15
- shutdown of nuclear, 108
- stirred-tank, 13
  - sequence, 15
    - common-sense solution for, 23
    - dimensionless equations for, 48
    - graphical solution of, 38
    - optimal problems for, 20
      - variants, 33

Reliability, structural, 100
Reliability theory, 100
Results, presentation of
- graphical, 42
- for stirred tanks, 30
- tabular, 31

ROBERTS, S. M., 95, 108, 136
RUDD, D. F., 100, 107, 108, 136

SAMUELSON, P. A., 12, 87
SARGENT, R. W. H., 117
Scarcity value, 56
SCARF, H., 87
SCHWARTZ, J. T., 8
Search methods
- general, 11
- gradient-free, 5
- random, 6

SHAPIRO, E., 117
SOLOW, R. M., 12
State
- in continuous problem, 112
- definition of, 17
- variables, 17
- vector, 17

Steepest ascent, method of, 4
STEVENS, W. F., 136

Temperature
- effect on reaction rate, 21
- equation for, in stirred tank, 21

TEN-DYKE, R. P., 107
Trajectories, optimal satellite, 107
Transformation
- in continuous problems, 112
- definition of, 18

Trends, control of economic, 72

VADJA, S., 11, 59
Variables
- dimensionless, 47
- reciprocal, 70

WANNINGER, L. A., 136
Water resources, 107
WESTBROOK, G. T., 108
WILDE, D. J., 11, 131
WILLIAMS, J. D., 12
WILSON, K. B., 11

ZENER, C., 59

Printed in the United States of America.